Bunty, the great new picture paper for girls, first saw the light of day on the 18th of January 1958 and very quickly became a favourite with youngsters all over the country. The thrilling mix of stories — and free ladybird ring — proved a winner and, for almost fifty years, the magazine continued to bring pleasure to generations of girls.

This treasury of stories and features, carefully selected from some of the early weekly and annual publications, is sure to bring memories flooding back, as women of all ages become reacquainted with old friends such as Moira Kent, Lorna Drake, Katy O'Connor and, of course, The Four Marys. There's also a chance to laugh with Toots, try your hand with Bunty's Cut-out Wardrobe and generally lose yourself in the many memorable stories and features.

All you have to do is pull up a chair and let yourself be transported back to the days of childhood and the magical world that was Bunty.

Printed and published in Great Britain by D.C. THOMSON & CO., LTD.,
185 Fleet Street, London EC4A 2HS. © D.C. THOMSON & CO., LTD., 2009.
ISBN 978-1-84535-384-1

# BUNTY

EVERY TUESDAY. Price 4ᴰ

# Nº 1
## OF A

# GREAT NEW
# PICTURE
# PAPER
# *for GIRLS*

## *Ladybird Ring* FREE Inside!

*There have been many memorable characters in the history of Bunty, but none have made such a big impact – or lasted as long – as the country's favourite schoolgirls …*

# The Four Marys

MARY RADLEIGH

MARY SIMPSON

MARY FIELD

MARY COTTER

THE Four Marys were Third Formers at St Elmo's School for Girls, and shared the same study in Bee's House. Shortly before the school broke up for Christmas, the girls went into Elmbury to try to get some ideas for presents.

I WANT YOU TO DRAW A BOWL OF FRUIT THIS MORNING. DON'T FORGET WHAT I'VE TAUGHT YOU ABOUT SHADING, GIRLS!

*Although their appearance changed slightly over the years, and their adventures altered with current fashions and trends, the four girls from differing backgrounds remained in the Third Form at St Elmo's School for Girls during their entire time in Bunty. They were not exactly ever present in the magazine, but there were very, very few weeks when they didn't appear and, at one time, they actually featured in picture and prose stories at the same time. Now that's popular!*

MY MOTHER WAS HERE AT ST ELMO'S WHEN SHE WAS A YOUNG GIRL. WE HAVE PICTURES OF HER AT HOME, AND SHE'S WEARING THE SAME UNIFORM AS I AM NOW! ISN'T IT ABOUT TIME WE HAD A CHANGE, DR GULL?

GRACIOUS! I'D ...GHT ABOUT

8.10.77 BTY

YES, IT'S DEFINITELY IN HERE!

MABEL'S STUDY!

Mabel Lentham and Veronica Laverly, a pair of snobbish, unpopular Third Formers, were in the Store.

*As well as the title characters, other memorable faces over the years included Miss Creef, their Form Teacher, Dr Gull, Headmistress, and the unforgettable snobs – Mabel and Veronica. Although Dr Gull was succeeded by the radical and outgoing Miss Mitchell in the eighties, the others were all in evidence right to the end.*

GOING TO HAVE A LUCKY DIP, MABEL?

DON'T BE UTTERLY, UTTERLY RIDICULOUS. THAT SORT OF SILLY THING IS ONLY FOR CHILDREN!

*Every Bunty reader has her own favourite Four Marys adventure, but now's your chance to take a step into the past and read the very first 'Marys' story from the very first issue of Bunty.*

Tuesday is " Bunty " day!

And so it all began!

# When you meet a girl wearing this badge you'll know that she's a member of

## Bunty Club

Thousands of girls from all over the country flocked to join the new club and proudly wear the Scottie dog badge. In return for a postal order worth 1s 6d, girls would receive – post free – their 'beautiful chromium and enamel' badge and a membership card which not only contained a membership certificate, but also gave details of the club secret mark and secret code. Later, there would be special coded messages and puzzles for club members only, with the chance to win prizes such as hockey sticks or postal orders.

### The Club's Secret Code

| | | | |
|---|---|---|---|
| A = G | H = N | O = U | V = B |
| B = H | I = O | P = V | W = C |
| C = I | J = P | Q = W | X = D |
| D = J | K = Q | R = X | Y = E |
| E = K | L = R | S = Y | Z = F |
| F = L | M = S | T = Z | |
| G = M | N = T | U = A | |

When writing a message in secret code instead of putting down A you put down G, for B put down H, for C put down I and so on. When reading a message in secret code, remember that G means A, H means B, A means U and so on. A code message will appear every week in Bunty.

## Bunty Club

MEMBERSHIP CARD

This is to certify that

.............................................

.............................................

.............................................

.............................................

is a member of the
**Bunty Club**

### Bunty Club SECRET MARK

WHEN writing letters to other club members, put the secret mark on the outside of your envelope up near the left-hand corner, and after your name in the letter. The secret mark, which is shown above, is an easy way of drawing the Bunty doggie.

MUUJ RAIQ ZU EUA

**A prized possession for many a girl was her Bunty Club membership card and badge.**

---

## BUNTY CLUB

### SPECIAL CODE MESSAGE FOR MEMBERS OF BUNTY CLUB ONLY

NUC CUARJ EUA ROQK ZU COT G RUBKRE
VXOFK? GRR EUA NGBK ZU JU OY ZU LOTJ ZNK
IUJK SKYYGMK NOJJKT OT UTK UL ZNOY CKKQ'Y
VOIZAXK YZUXOKY, CXOZK OZ JUCT OT KTMROYN,
GTJ YKTJ OZ ZU ZNK LURRUCOTM GJJXKYY.

Send your entry right away to:—
SPOT THE MESSAGE (Competition No. 3),
BUNTY CLUB,
P.O. BOX 72,
186 FLEET STREET,
LONDON, E.C.4.

G SGTOIAXK YKZ CORR HK YKTZ ZU ZNK LOXYZ
MOXR ZU YKTJ OT G IUXXKIZ KTZXE.

### FOR THOSE WHO WANT TO JOIN.

Send a postal order for the membership fee of 1s 6d. Make the postal order payable to BUNTY at LONDON Post Office by writing these words in the spaces provided, and cross the postal order with two heavy ink lines /&Co./.

Also send your full name, address and age written in block letters.

You don't need to send a stamp, only the postal order and your name, address and age.

Do not enclose coins.

Send your letter to—
BUNTY CLUB,
P.O. BOX 72,
186 FLEET STREET,
LONDON, E.C.4.

The postage on all letters is 3d.

You will then be sent, post free, your membership letter with the club's secret code, secret mark and the beautiful chromium and enamel badge.

# COSY CORNER

**COSY CORNER was fronted by Jenny Wren and, in return for having a letter printed in Bunty, girls could win their choice of the prizes shown here – plus a beautiful 'Bunty' scarf. It was the must-have of its day!**

Jenny Wren offers you splendid [pri]zes for a funny conundrum, a [go]od joke, a handy tip—in fact any[th]ing you think will interest other [gi]rls. She offers you your choice of [th]e following prizes—

[P]EN AND PENCIL SET, POSTAL [ORD]ER, STRING OF PEARLS, [MA]NICURE SET, GIRL'S WALLET.

In addition, each winner will also receive a beautiful "BUNTY" SCARF. Send your entries, naming the prize you fancy, to—"COSY CORNER," "BUNTY," 12 FETTER LANE, FLEET STREET, LONDON, E.C.4. At the end of your letter please write the titles of your TWO favourite "Bunty" picture stories.

## MOUSE TRAP.
Motorist—"I've just killed your cat and I've come to replace it."

Lady—"Very well then, but do you think you can catch mice?"

—"Bunty" scarf and postal order to Carol Cornwell, 22 Grizedale Cres., Ribbleton, Preston, Lancashire.

⋆ ⋆

## WHAT A HEN!

her cheeks.

The onion, then she peels.

—"Bunty" scarf and postal order to Patricia Gaines, 127 Macalpine Road, Dundee, Angus.

⋆ ⋆

## HAVE YOU A CAT?
Cats should have a box or basket of their own. One of a reasonable size with short legs to keep it from floor-draughts is best. Line it with several layers of brown paper and fold an old blanket into a snug mattress. Your cat will then be nice and cosy.

—"Bunty" scarf and wallet to C. M. Cooper, 73 The Woodlands, Birkenhead, Cheshire.

⋆ ⋆

## HAVE A TRY

There were 12 books on a bookshelf. If each book was an inch thick, and a bookworm started to eat his way through the books, starting at page one in the first book and ending at the last page in the last book, how many inches would he eat through?

*Answer—10 inches.*

—"Bunty" scarf and manicure set to Pauline Wilson, 41 Erroll Rd., Hove, 3, Sussex.

## A Chance to Win TWO PRIZES

An elegant pen and pencil set that will make you the envy of all your school chums

A roomy wallet with many compartments. It even has a calendar for EVERY year

Every winner in [J]enny Wren's 'Cosy Corner' receives a beautiful "Bunty" scarf in colourful tartan. In addition she has the choice of any one of the five prizes shown here. Why don't YOU have a try for these prizes? You'll find out what you have to do, on Page 6.

A delightful manicure set for you to carry around.

The perfect pearl necklace to wear at any party.

If you would rather buy your own prize, then a postal order is just what you're looking for.

## DRESS SENSE.
Buy two ribbons the same length and breadth. One of these ribbons should be the colour of the coat you will be wearing and the other the colour of your dress. Oversew these neatly along the edges firmly together, then sew a piece of elastic to the ends. When you go to a party or any other place, you can have one side the colour of your coat, and when you get there, you can turn it to the colour of your dress.

—"Bunty" scarf and pen and pencil set to Margaret McQuillan, 8 Croft Road, Brampton, Cumberland.

⋆ ⋆

## Did You Write?
*Many of you have written nice letters to Cosy Corner and we want you all to know we've enjoyed reading them. This is us thanking all of you who sent a letter.*

Jenny Wren
and
The Editor.

## POSTMAN OR SAILOR?
Postmen don't always walk [w]hen they make their deliveries ! [I]n the low-lying country of the [F]ens, in Eastern England, you [c]an see a postman doing part [o]f his round by rowing-boat.

—"Bunty" scarf and wallet to [J]acqueline Eldridge, 26 Uplands Road, [O]adby, Leicester.

⋆ ⋆

What bird does a happy dog [r]epresent?

*Answer—The wagtail.*

—"Bunty" scarf and manicure set to [M]ary McCormack, 36 Jonathan Street, [V]auxhall, London, S.E.11.

⋆ ⋆

## ARM MEASURE.
There was no such thing as a [y]ard measure until Henry 1st [c]ame to the throne. Then, he got [th]e idea that to find a yard you [w]ould measure from the top of [th]e arm to the bottom of the [fi]ngertips, and that would be [c]alled a yard, so if you have a [l]ong arm you would have a [l]onger yard than a person with [a] small arm.

—"Bunty" scarf and postal order to Patricia Connolly, 38 Manxmoor Road, Blackburn, Lancs.

sea it looks like a [...] rainbow. The sea anemone is related to the jelly-fish and coral.

—"Bunty" scarf and manicure set to Pauline Randall, 153 Gordon Road, Chatham, Kent.

What is closed [...] and open when closed?

*A swingbridge or drawbridge.*

—"Bunty" scarf and postal order to Kay L. Jenkins, 4 Eagles Place, Blaen-y-Maes, Swansea.

## JENNY WREN'S EYE SPY TEST

Study this picture for three minutes, then turn to Page 12 and try to answer the questions there. No prizes are offered, but you and your friends can have lots of fun testing your memory.

# THE DANCING LIFE of MOIRA KENT

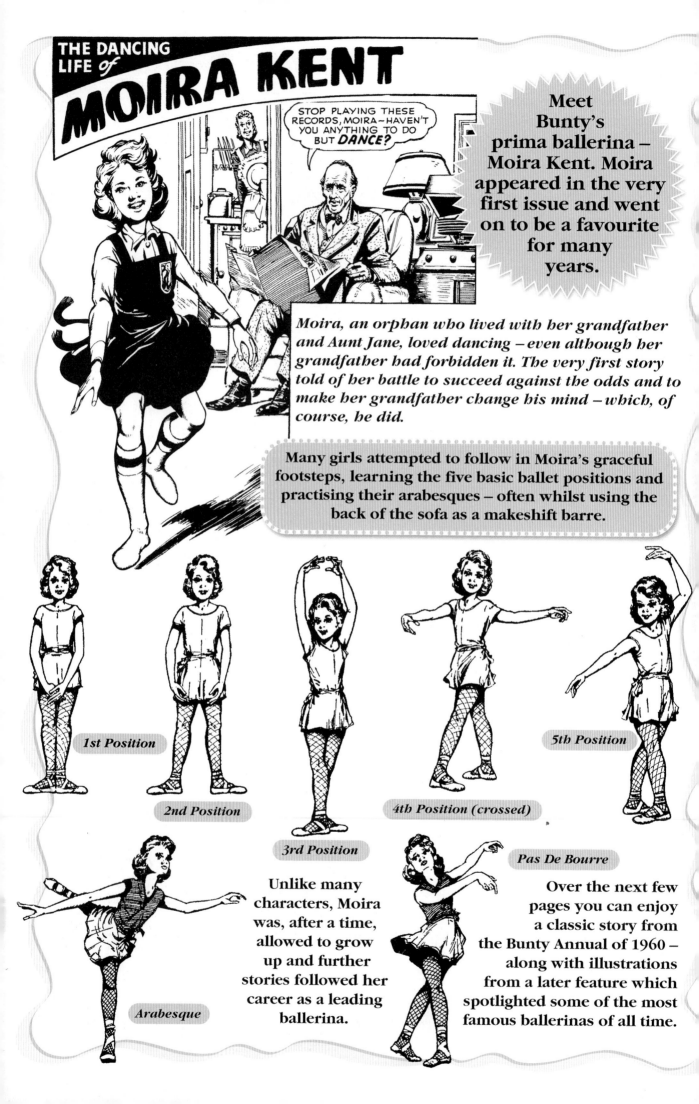

STOP PLAYING THESE RECORDS, MOIRA—HAVEN'T YOU ANYTHING TO DO BUT *DANCE?*

Meet Bunty's prima ballerina – Moira Kent. Moira appeared in the very first issue and went on to be a favourite for many years.

Moira, an orphan who lived with her grandfather and Aunt Jane, loved dancing – even although her grandfather had forbidden it. The very first story told of her battle to succeed against the odds and to make her grandfather change his mind – which, of course, he did.

Many girls attempted to follow in Moira's graceful footsteps, learning the five basic ballet positions and practising their arabesques – often whilst using the back of the sofa as a makeshift barre.

*1st Position*

*2nd Position*

*3rd Position*

*4th Position (crossed)*

*5th Position*

*Pas De Bourre*

*Arabesque*

Unlike many characters, Moira was, after a time, allowed to grow up and further stories followed her career as a leading ballerina.

Over the next few pages you can enjoy a classic story from the Bunty Annual of 1960 – along with illustrations from a later feature which spotlighted some of the most famous ballerinas of all time.

# THE DANCING LIFE OF MOIRA KENT

**M**OIRA KENT, of the Globe Ballet Company, was acclaimed as one of the finest ballerinas in the world. Her brilliant execution, allied to a natural grace and youthful charm, made her a favourite with the audiences which packed the Globe Theatre for every performance.

One day, after an exhausting dress rehearsal, Moira left the theatre. Her Grandpa, Matthew Martin, was waiting for her in his old car—but he wasn't alone.

OH, NO! AUTOGRAPH HUNTERS!

STAGE DOOR

*Inspiration for story titles came from the most unlikely places. This tale from the early eighties clearly drew its inspiration from the 'Paint Your Wagon' song made famous by Lee Marvin.*

*Where the inspiration for the girls' unusual mode of transport came from, however, isn't quite as obvious.*

Prose stories were prominent in early issues of Bunty, with at least two stories – often of three pages – usually included in each weekly magazine.
The stories covered a variety of subjects – both happy and harrowing – and many of these characters went on to star in the more visual picture stories.

★ Irene's greatest test—playing in the mighty Albert Hall ★

# LITTLE MISS FEATHER-FINGERS

WITH an accent of surprise in her voice, Miss Broadley said sharply, "Irene, you are not paying attention this afternoon."

Irene Pryce blushed furiously and sat up with a guilty look. She looked at her schoolteacher apologetically.

"Do you know what I was talking about?" went on the teacher.

"I'm afraid not, Miss Broadley," said Irene, standing up. "I must have been dreaming. I'm very sorry."

"Wait behind after school," said the teacher severely, while the other girls smirked.

Irene Pryce, a London orphan, had been boarded out for three years with a foster-mother in the tiny Yorkshire village of Lassdale.

During most of that time, she had lived in the cottage of a frail but charming old lady, Mrs Heslin. But Mrs Heslin had died, and now Irene was living with Mrs Greer.

As soon as school dismissed, Miss Broadley went over to the little, dark-haired girl with the large grey eyes. She put an affectionate arm on her shoulder.

"I see it's your thirteenth birthday today, Irene," said the schoolteacher with a gentle smile. "I've been looking up the class register. Many happy returns!"

The kindness of the tone was too much for poor Irene. She put her head on her desk and burst into floods of tears.

"There, there!" said Miss Broadley softly, after the storm had subsided. "Suppose you tell me all about it? Tell me why you're so tired that you f... asleep in class. Tell me why your pian...

quick and clever. The g... discovered part of Madame's story. She was a famous concert pianist who had retired to the seclusion of the Yorkshire village after her artist husband and her little daughter met with an accident.

"What is this?" yelled Madame. She

★ A new pal for you—a girl who devotes her life to animals ★

# Lindy Martin

THE ANIMALS' FRIEND

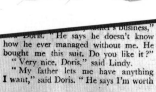

LINDY MARTIN stopped the small van and got out. Painted on the side of the van were the words Animals Protection Society. Lindy worked for the society, and it was her job to go to the help of any animal or bird in trouble.

Lindy opened the b...

it to him in the business. He's promised me a fur coat for my birthday."

"You are lucky!" said Lindy.

"I can't decide which to have," said Doris. "I like beaver and Persian lamb. And there's always mink, of course."

"Mink every time, Doris!" smiled Lindy.

...came bursting ...gate. They sur-...ing together. ...y?"

...n?"

...oise by barking ...gan to retreat. ...u stick a job ...ared.

...some-... ...t and ...s, but in

...d led the ...children's ...meet her. ...oungsters, ... dog. ...d. "He ...d to help

...Doris. "He says he doesn't know how he ever managed without me. He bought me this suit. Do you like it?"

"Very nice, Doris," said Lindy.

"My father lets me have anything I want," said Doris. "He says I'm worth

when it was first brought in to the A.P.S. kennels. This was the happy end to another story. Lindy was enjoying herself a lot more than Doris and her fur coats.

## The Gasping Goldfish.

WHEN Lindy got back to the A.P.S. headquarters she found another job waiting for her.

"Some old lady rang up," said Mr Green, the inspector in charge. "She wants us to do something about her goldfish."

"What's wrong with them?" asked Lindy. She was used to getting odd requests from people.

"She wants them protected," said Mr Green. "I couldn't get much out of her. You know how excited people get on the phone. But apparently something attacked them! You'd better go round and see what you can do, Lindy."

Lindy drove in the van to the address that Mr Green gave her. An elderly woman looked at her doubtfully when the door opened.

"You're very young, aren't you?" said the woman.

"I've got a fair amount of training and experience," smiled Lindy.

"Well, I hope you can do something about my poor little fish," said the woman, whose name was Mrs Webb.

She took Lindy into her living-room. Two goldfish were swimming about in a jam jar. On the floor by the window were the broken remains of a goldfish bowl.

"I left the pieces there so that you could see," said Mrs Webb. "Evidence, you know. It was my next-door neighbour's cat!"

"Are you sure of that?" said Lindy.

"What else could it be?" demanded

... A.P.S. always made sure that people who offered to take a stray dog were the right sort to have pets. Lindy knew that in this house the dog would have a good home.

Watching the children romping with the dog on the lawn, Lindy remembered how lost and forlorn the dog had been

## ★ Carole sings her best— for a photograph ★
# The GIRL with the GOLDEN VOICE

the back door of their home she heard her

think you have great talent. They spoke to Mr Tattersall about you. And now,

. . . of Madame . . . owner.
. . . ole at once. . . . She sings at . . . aces."
. . . s that she has . . . om here, just . . . Mr Tattersall . . . onths she will

. . . to give you . . . orbes trium-

. . . unable to say . . . aye's eye. Her . . . ut her eyes

. . . e a week for . . . Mr Tattersall. . . . half-past four . . . ys. Can you

. . ," said Kaye, . . . hing eyes on . . . back. Go, by

. . . I'll be there . . . role joyfully. . . . verything she . . . ugh."
. . . said Captain

visitors out.

"He's at Bombay and will be leavin . . . soon for Perth, in Australia," Kaye sai . . . "It's a shame that dear Carole do . . . not see her father more often."

"Yes, the sea is a hard life," sai . . . Mr Tattersall with a smile. " But Fran . . . Chatton will be proud of his daughte . . . when he comes home."

The door closed, and Carole picke . . . up the tray with the teacups on it, . . . take it into the kitchen.

### The Real Kaye.

HEN Kaye flew in. Sh . . . rushed across to her fai . . . haired, thirteen-year-ol . . . stepdaughter and slappe . . . her viciously on both cheeks. S . . . savage was the attack that Caro . . . dropped the tray.

"You little beast!" screamed Kay . . . Chatton, her eyes blazing. "To g . . . cringing behind my back, borrowin . . . a dress, making up to those peopl . . . defying me. I'll make you pay fo . . . this, my girl."

Carole, with great red marks on he . . . white cheeks, faced her angry ste . . . mother calmly, though her hea . . . was pounding.

"But, Kaye, I thought you seeme . . . pleased——" she began.

---

## ★ The return of your favourite soldier—Sally Howard of the A.T.S. ★
# LANCE-CORPORAL SALLY

A PARADE was taking place at 095 Mixed Heavy Anti-Aircraft Battery. Royal Artillery gunners and girls of the Auxiliary Territorial Service were drawn up to attention in their sections. Dressed alike in khaki battle-dress, they looked like rows of nine-pins.

The gun-site was one of a ring guarding an important British manu-facturing town against the enemy bombers of World War Two. Because of the shortage of manpower, girls of the A.T.S., the women's branch of the army, operated the instruments which directed the fire of the big guns.

The daily inspection was over, and non-commissioned officers were being detailed by the officers to take charge of the various gun-training, drill and fatigue parties.

" Lance-Corporal Howard !"

Sally Howard stepped smartly forward out of the ranks and halted in front of the A.T.S. Subaltern, Miss Mercer. The air of confidence that she wore hid her fear. As the newness of her stripe testified, she had only been recently promoted and she was finding the duties and responsibilities of an n.c.o. tough going.

Now she listened nervously for her orders.

"You will take those girls who are not manning the guns or on fatigues and give them half an hour's marching drill," announced Miss Mercer.

Sally's heart bumped down, for she had had little experience as . . .

right . . . Their . . . excus . . .

Bo . . . Mile . . . ing . . . envi . . . auth . . .

A . . . whi . . . Du . . . by . . .

sq . . . th . . . gir . . . gl . . .

jo . . .

v . . .

She got the squ . . . marching again. It was a quiet, residentia . . . road with little traffic, but, of course, the inevitable errand boy was passing and stopped to stare.

had joined the audien . . . uproariously at each command. Com-peting with the dog and the noise of the girls made her hoarse, and the squad seized upon this as a fresh excuse for mis-behaviour. They pretended to mis-

### Sally takes her first drill look

---

## ★ A tin of oats helps Pimpernel get used to motor cars ★
# PIMPERNEL The HORSE with a FUTURE

IMPERNEL, a good-look-ing chestnut yearling colt, jumped backwards away from the car . . .

in the yard, and all the boxes were full.

In summer the yard was very attractive, for there wa . . . . . . t oak tree on the . . . ut as the weather . . . e tree was bare . . . and brown.

. . . o the box quickly . . . sheet for a thick . . . on burying his . . . feed.

. . . im once again . . . e after she had . . . dock. Pimpernel . . . ut he did allow . . . the day before. . . . , he spied the . . . e bonnet. He . . . rcise and was . . . the oats. He . . . the car and . . . ds the tin. . . . when he got . . . and into the . . . ht of the oats . . . was too much . . . ied forward . . . oats.

. . . f mouthfuls . . . unting him, . . . o the other

. . . t the car . . . necessary, . . . ng another . . . e reached

. . . an, came . . . on with . . . approval . . . f the tin. . . . coit too quickly

. . . breaker, Jill and . . . mpernel had progressed amazingly . . . well, up to the traffic incident.

Jill led Pimpernel away from the car . . . back to his loose-box in the spacious . . . stableyard. There was room for forty horses

. . . and left the car alone after Pimpernel . . . had eaten the oats till the next day. But, . . . each morning she took the colt up to the . . . car after exercise to get his reward of . . . oats. Soon Pimpernel took no notice of . . . the car, but dived his nose greedily into . . . the oats.

When Matt Nichols saw how well J . . . had progressed with Pimpernel, . . . decided to drive the car slowly towar . . . the colt the next time, to get him us . . . to a moving vehicle again.

Pimpernel took no notice at all whe . . . the car was driven slowly towards hi . . . He waited, standing beside Jill till t . . . car stopped, then he reached forward . . . take the oats.

"Right, now get up on him, Jill . . . said Matt Nichols, a tall, well-dresse . . . man with a pleasant face, "and ri . . . him towards me as I drive the car."

He got out of the car and gave J . . . a leg up into the saddle. Pimpernel sto . . . well while Jill settled herself in the sad . . . and slipped her feet into the stirru . . . Then she turned him and rode him aw . . . from the car down the drive.

When Pimpernel faced the movi . . . car again with Jill on his back, he walk . . . towards it without any fear at all.

They tried the same performan . . . several times, with the car coming fas . . . each time. Pimpernel did not turn a ha . . . For the last time Matt drove the c . . . straight past the colt quite fast, and th . . . turned it round and drove up behind hi . . .

"Well done, Jill," called out Ma . . . as he went past.

Matt came into Pimpernel's loose-b . . . when Jill was taking his tack off and t . . . her of his plans for the next day. He w . . . going to try Pimpernel with the horse-b . . . instead of the car.

### Steady Does It.

ILL led Pimpernel up . . . the horse-box, where . . . tin of oats was tied secure . . . on to one of the win . . . The colt stopped dead when he g . . . near the box, and was just about . . . whip round when he spotted the . . . of oats.

That made him change his mi . . .

# A Star Role for Sally

**S**ALLY MARTIN'S hand shook slightly as she took the thermometer from Ronnie's mouth and held it up to the light. As she had expected, his temperature was rising.

She felt a sharp stab of fear. Her small brother was ill, she told herself, very ill.

His brown eyes were bright with fever and his normally chubby face pinched and white with pain. His breathing was rapid and shallow, and he turned his head from side to side on his pillow as the pain got worse.

If only she had taken notice earlier, Sally reproached herself. He had been irritable and off-colour for a few days now. She had put it down to his missing Mum and Dad, and to the intense heat that had broken only a few hours earlier in a violent storm.

Sally moved wearily away from Ronnie's bedside and slumped down in a chair. Ronnie meant so much to Mum and Dad, her thoughts ran on, and she felt a lump form in her throat.

She had been fourteen when he was born four years ago, and she had been almost as excited as her parents at his arrival.

Why hadn't she called the doctor in sooner, she asked herself, her pretty, heart-shaped face drawn with anxiety.

She had been trusted to look after Ronnie while her parents were away in London for a few days, and she had let them and Ronnie down.

And all because she had been so wrapped up in learning her lines for her part in the Drama School's next production.

It had been a thrill to be given a decent part and she had wanted to play it exceptionally well. Ronnie's whining had irritated her, and she had told him to go away and play.

Sally felt her blue eyes fill with tears and impatiently brushed them away. It was no use sitting here and reproaching herself, she told herself determinedly. She had to do something for Ronnie and do it quickly.

With a last look at her brother, she closed the bedroom door quietly and went downstairs to the telephone. She would try again for the doctor.

The last time there had been no reply—if she could not get through to him now, she would dial 999.

It was a few minutes before Sally realised that the line was dead. Then, in a panic, she banged the rest up and down and called "Operator" in a high-pitched voice, quite unlike her usual, rather calm, slow way of speaking.

When finally she replaced the receiver she was very pale. The storm must have blown down the wires, she told herself—and their nearest neighbour was five miles away.

A remote country cottage may be the ideal place for Father to write his plays, she reflected dismally, but at times like this, one longed for the bustle of a town.

**W**ITH a sigh, Sally moved away from the useless telephone and went towards the kitchen. An extra-loud crash of thunder, followed by an almost blinding flash of lightning, made her falter.

All her life she had been afraid of storms.

Making a great effort to sound calm she called to Mrs Briggs, their general help.

"Mrs Briggs," she called. "I'm going to fetch the doctor for Ronnie. I can't get him on the telephone—I think the wires are down. I'll take the car."

Sally was shaking when at last she got to the garage and eased herself behind the steering wheel of the car.

When she realised that the car was not going to start, she experienced a moment of sheer despair. Everything seemed to be working against her. She remembered now that her father had mentioned the car needed attention.

Sally's fair head drooped and she rested her forehead against the steering wheel. She was beaten—how could she walk the five miles to the village in this awful storm?

A small voice inside her reminded her that if she went through the woods she would cut off almost three miles of the walk.

Sally felt a great shudder go through her at the thought. It would be dangerous in the woods in a storm.

"But I've got to do it," she murmured aloud and climbed shakily from the car and went out on to the drive.

She could see a light burning in Ronnie's room.

Ronnie was depending on her, she told herself. He needed help, and it was up to her to get it for him.

"It's the star role, Sally," she said aloud as she walked down the drive and stood in the narrow country road. "The stage is all yours!"

 ALLY's stomach gave a sickening lurch as she crossed over and into the woods, and her lips trembled as she moved amongst the tall trees.

Again and again the vivid lightning flashed, lighting up her path and making her flinch with fear.

A couple of times she stumbled and almost fell. She tried to hurry, but fear seemed to be weighting down her limbs and making her clumsy and slow.

The third time Sally stumbled she really lost her balance and went down with a sickening thud. For a moment she lay stunned until a sharp pain ran through her right leg and jerked her into full consciousness.

She moved slightly and dragged herself into a sitting position, talking away light-headedly to herself as she did so.

"This wasn't in the script," she muttered. And then. "A good actress is prepared to cope with the unexpected, to improvise and still achieve a smooth performance."

She pulled herself to her feet, crying out at the pain the movement caused her, and stood for a moment, swaying unsteadily and ashen-faced.

She began to argue with herself. Home was still nearer than the village. She could drag herself back there.

Perhaps Ronnie was better now—children did run high fevers over quite small things. She had heard her mother say so.

But Sally could not convince herself. The memory of Ronnie's pain-racked face was too strong.

"Get on, Sally Martin," she said loudly. "You're holding up the show."

After what seemed an eternity to Sally, she saw lights — the lights of the houses in the village. Fighting against her increasing weakness, she moved painfully towards them.

Her leg felt as though it was on fire and the storm was as violent as ever.

Strangely, Sally found she could ignore the storm now. Her determination to get help for Ronnie had reached the point where neither storm nor pain could hold her back.

A car picked her out in its headlights as she stumbled into the road at the outskirts of the village. She managed to blurt out her message to

the driver and then collapsed into his arms.

 HEN Sally regained consciousness she was in a strange bed and her right leg felt heavy and cold. She gave a small cry of alarm and opened her eyes to find her mother and father bending over her.

"It's all right, darling," her mother said quickly. "You are in hospital and have broken your leg. But you are quite safe now."

"Ronnie," Sally whispered. "Ronnie! Is he—is he all right?"

"Fine," her father said cheerfully. "In the next ward, minus his appendix and nagging the nurses for something to eat!"

Sally let out a sigh of relief and relaxed against her pillows. Looking up, she saw the pride shining in her parents' eyes and flushed a little.

"Ronnie had been ill for days," she said honestly. "I should have done something about it sooner."

Her mother gripped one of her hands and her father the other—and the pride was still in their faces.

"Sal," her father said quietly. "You've always been so frightened of storms. The one last night was a real snorter from all accounts. And yet you went out in it."

"I had to," Sally said soberly. A faint smile lit her eyes. "And to help me I pretended I was playing a part in a play. The star part, and I had to play it really well. And after a while the storm didn't frighten me—it was just part of the sound effects."

Her voice trailed off and she yawned loudly.

"Go to sleep again," her mother said gently and bent and kissed her on the forehead.

"I will," Sally murmured contentedly and before her heavy eyelids closed, she smiled and added—"Curtains! The show is over!"

✶ ✶ ✶ ✶ ✶ ✶ ✶ ✶ ✶ ✶ ✶ ✶ ✶ ✶ ✶ ✶ ✶ ✶

*In the early days, many Bunty heroines were young girls setting out on their first job. Characters such as those shown here seemed glamorous and exciting to young readers – and a million miles away from reality.*

★ Wendy's job takes her to the pyramids by camel! ★

**WENDY ROUND the WORLD**

YOU'RE BEING SENT ON A SPECIALLY-CHARTERED FLIGHT, WENDY—STAYING OVERNIGHT IN EGYPT.

I CERTAINLY GET AROUND IN THIS JOB!

SIXTEEN-YEAR-OLD Wendy Brown had an unusual and exciting job—Junior Air Hostess with Star Airlines. It was her duty to look after children travelling alone and to cope with any problems connected with them.

**PATTI MASON — Fashion Model**

PATTI MASON, a junior model, worked for James Lennard, a fashion designer who had recently started his own couture house in London. One day, Patti posed for advertising photographs of Lennard's winter sports wear.

I HAVEN'T A HEAD FOR HEIGHTS!

**Debbie Lane STUDENT NURSE**

I'M FEELING DREADFUL!

DEBBIE LANE was training as a nurse St Agnes Hospital, and although had to work and study hard, she was h in her chosen career. One day the S Tutor took a group of students to obse simple nasal operation from the ope theatre gallery. Just after the oper began, Debbie felt sick and fain

★ Can the Good Fairy's magic remove

**The Good Fairy**

SIXTEEN-YEAR-OLD Grace James was given a wonderful job with a firm which was launching an advertising campaign for a new product. She was to be a real-life Good Fairy, granting the wishes of children who wrote in to her!

**Miss Fix-It of TV**

YOUNG Meg Newton, who was known at the TV studios as Little Miss Fix-It, was travelling to Devon with a TV producer, Eric Dale. They were going to film the English village of Dellcroft.

MY NOSE IS HORRIB

# HAIRDRESSER ON WHEELS

**NOW, N...** SHAMPOO... LET'S H...

## Flower Shop Flora

WILL YOU REPEAT THAT, SIR? YES, THAT'S WHAT I THOUGHT YOU SAID. RIGHT, SIR, BY THREE O'CLOCK SHARP.

FLORA ROBBINS was senior assistant at Miss Bingley's flower shop in Dartwell. One morning, Flora took an order for roses.

## Anne Proctor — ANIMAL DOCTOR

NINETEEN-YEAR-OLD Anne Proctor was the assistant veterinary surgeon at Stamford's Circus. Anne had been at the circus for several months, and her cheerful ...th the animals made

GOSH, ROSALIE! LOOK AT POPPA GRONCHO UP THERE! AND HE HASN'T A SAFETY-NET EITHER!

I KNOW! HOW WOULD YOU LIKE TO BE A TIGHTROPE WALKER, ANNE?

## ⭐ She has the tip-toppest job of all for girls. ⭐
# Lyn Raymond — AIR STEWARDESS

**Only Two Vacancies.**

LYN RAYMOND walked slowly down the hall to where the letter lay on the door mat. She could see the monogram of Astral Airways on the envelope. This was the reply she had been so eagerly awaiting for the last three weeks, and now it had come she could hardly bear to open it.

Lyn was a young student nurse at the local Cottage Hospital and had applied for a job as air stewardess with Astral Airways, a British charter company operating from London.

When she first wrote to them, she ...the other applicants being models or debutantes, sleek and sophisticated.

She sighed deeply and drew on her gloves for the last time, as the coach drew to a halt outside the Astral Airways building.

As she opened the waiting-room door in Astral Airways' newly-built staff ...

don't call me soon I'll go and have word with his secretary. What's yo... foreign language?"

"Oh, and ...you speak ? ...time to rep... ...n put his hea...

...ve been expec... ...ome this wa...

...and her spir... ...the other gi... ...at there we... ...fteen girls we... ...se two place... ...at blonde g... ...ruefully. Th... ...een all the re...

...Man.

...e other gir... ...want to ...n, so Lyn sto... ...ndered to t... ...rt runwa... ...reched away... the distan... behind the flat-roofed buildings.

Everywhere was feverish activit... Small radio vans rushed hither a... thither, engineers in grease-stain... overalls were working in the hanga... and uniformed staff hurried in a...

*And then, of course, there was the girl with what was described as 'the tip-toppest job of all for girls' – Lyn Raymond. Her high flying adventures began in prose form before going on to be a favourite picture story for many years.*

As Lyn served up some snacks, she purposely dropped her lipstick.

It rolled right down the passageway. Now it was time for Lyn to put her plan into action.

Lyn returned to the pantry, racking her brains to form some plan of campaign. She realised that her job called for resourcefulness and initiative, but this was a tricky problem. After ruminating awhile, she hit on an idea.

As he removed his newspaper to strap on his safety belt, Lyn got a good look at Grumpy Joe's face—he answered the description of the jewel thief!

The sleek aircraft came in to make a perfect landing.

As the passengers left the plane, Lyn pointed to the suspect.

# It's "PLANE" Sailing —Thanks to the air stewardess

ALWAYS charming and well-groomed, the air stewardess is at the travellers' beck and call during every minute a plane is airborne.

She must have a large store of patience and good humour to deal with awkward passengers who are ready to find faults.

Sight-seeing in foreign lands.

She must also have a certain knowledge of children and nursing, and be able to relieve mothers who are at their wits' end with babies who can't settle down in their strange surroundings.

Ski-ing at the winter playgrounds of the world.

Meeting film stars and other famous personalities.

But an air stewardess's life is not all drudgery. Here are a few of the things which help to lighten her load and brighten her life on and off duty.

Bathing in the sun-drenched waters of the Mediterranean.

Another flight is over and the air stewardess sets off for home, perhaps to dream of the wonderful sights seen or to wonder what new thrills the next day's flight will bring.

# '60s

Some colourful covers from the 1960s. Bunty's older, unnamed, sister featured on a few early copies and a younger sister, Maisie, appeared for a time later.

*High kickin' capers to welcome in a new year.*

*A sparkling free gift for sparkling girls.*

No. 573–JANUARY 4, 1969

# BUNTY

EVERY TUESDAY. PRICE 5d.

A HAPPY NEW YEAR TO ALL OUR READERS

"Right!" says Bunty. "Off we go,
We've got to practise for the show."

The show is on, and kicking high,
See Bunty lead the dancers by.

No. 402–SEPT. 25. 1965

# BUNTY

EVERY TUESDAY. PRICE 5d.

FREE Inside

The TWINKLE RING

It twinkles like a star on your finger!

No. 582–MARCH 8. 1969

# BUNTY

EVERY TUESDAY. PRICE 6d.

See Bunty collect a doggy friend,
She's keeping him for the week-end.

And now she thinks, "Oh, what a shame!
Those children can't join in the game."

...o they greet our friend with glee?
...happy now as you can see.

*Smiling in the snow in 1969.*

They feel as if it isn't fair,
These little kids are really gay—
Riding on their super sleigh!

STANLEY PARK SECONDARY
MODERN SCHOOL (LIVERPOOL)

TYNEFIELD SCHOOL (PENRITH)

ELMHURST PREPARATORY
SCHOOL (CAMBORNE)

SHAW HOUSE SECONDARY
MODERN GIRLS' SCHOOL
(NEWBURY)

# Is Your School Badge On This Page?

HASSENBROOK COUNTY
SECONDARY SCHOOL
(STANFORD-LE-HOPE)

WILLESBOROUGH COUNTY
PRIMARY SCHOOL (ASHFORD)

WHITEHALL SCHOOL (LEICESTER)

CHRISTCHURCH SECONDARY
MODERN SCHOOL FOR GIRLS
(CHATHAM)

ST. JOSEPH'S SCHOOL
(WALTHAM CROSS)

SEAFIELD SCHOOL (ELGIN)

NOTRE DAME HIGH SCHOOL
FOR GIRLS (WIGAN)

EASTBANK SENIOR SECONDARY
SCHOOL (GLASGOW)

WESTBOROUGH HIGH SCHOOL
FOR GIRLS (WESTCLIFF-ON-SEA)

Hardship and misery formed the basis of many popular and long running stories – with 'The Children's Champion' being a perfect example. Poverty and disease may have haunted the backstreets of Victorian London, but they would prove no barrier to wealthy young Hester Langley as she set out to help the waifs and strays.

The story of Hester Langley and the homeless waifs of old London.

# The Children's Champion

WHAT A BORING EVENING THIS HAS BEEN. GENERAL BURROWS WAS BAD-TEMPERED AS USUAL, HIS WIFE COULD TALK OF NOTHING BUT HER DIFFICULTY IN GETTING GOOD SERVANTS, AND THEIR DAUGHTER SAT WITH HER MOUTH OPEN.

EIGHTEEN-YEAR-OLD Hester Langley, born in the year 1850, was the only daughter of rich, titled parents, Lord and Lady Langley, and she had received every advantage since birth.

Late one winter's night, Hester stood at the drawing-room windows of the Langley's town house in London's Elbury Square. As she watched their dinner guests depart, Hester reflected on how dissatisfied she was with her life.

Just then, Hester's parents entered the room.

HESTER—COME AWAY FROM THE WINDOW! SUCH MANNERS!

YOU HARDLY SPOKE A WORD ALL EVENING. OUR GUESTS NOTICED IT!

I'M SORRY, PAPA. I HAD A SLIGHT HEADACHE. IF YOU WILL EXCUSE ME, I WILL RETIRE.

TOMORROW WILL BE AS BORING AS TODAY. RIDING IN THE PARK IN THE MORNING, A SINGING LESSON IN THE AFTERNOON AND ANOTHER DINNER PARTY IN THE EVENING. IT'S ALL SO MUCH THE SAME— AND SO POINTLESS!

THERE'S THE HALL CLOCK STRIKING TWO AND I CANNOT GET TO SLEEP! I'M TOO RESTLESS.

I'LL GET THAT BOOK I WAS READING FROM THE MORNING ROOM. PERHAPS I CAN READ MYSELF TO SLEEP.

In the morning room, Hester was picking up her book when a sudden sound startled her.

I AM QUITE SURE I HEARD SOMEONE SNEEZE IN THE CONSERVATORY! WHO COULD BE THERE AT THIS TIME OF NIGHT? SHALL I ROUSE THE SERVANTS?

NO, I WON'T! I'LL LOOK FOR MYSELF! I'D BETTER TAKE A WEAPON WITH ME. A POKER WILL DO!

ATISHOOO!

C-COME OUT FROM THERE A-AT ONCE! I HAVE A WEAPON!

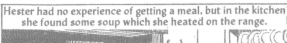

Hester had no experience of getting a meal, but in the kitchen she found some soup which she heated on the range.

Annie explained that she and the other children lived and slept in the back streets and alleys. They earned an occasional copper by running errands for the shopkeepers, or by minding a horse while its owner was in a shop. They raided the pig-swill bins for scraps, and some of the bolder among them stole food when they saw the chance.

Polly was aghast when Hester explained what she was going to do.

OH, MISS! YOU CAN'T—BEGGING YOUR PARDON FOR THE LIBERTY. YOU'LL BE SET UPON—YOU'LL BE MURDERED!

NO. I WON'T, POLLY—NOT IF YOU LEND ME SOME OF YOUR CLOTHES SO THAT I DON'T LOOK LIKE A-ER-A NOB.

Polly relented, and ten minutes later, Hester was ready.

WELL, POLLY? WILL I PASS?

YES, MISS, BUT OH! I SHAN'T REST UNTIL YOU ARE BACK!

YOU SAY STEPNEY IS A LONG WAY FROM HERE, ANNIE, SO I THINK WE WILL GO BY HANSOM CAB. THERE'S SURE TO BE ONE ABOUT.

COO—ME IN A HANSOM!

WHAT'S A YOUNG LADY LIKE YOU GOING TO STEPNEY AT THIS TIME OF NIGHT FOR? YOU SURE YOU GOT ENOUGH FOR THE FARE?

OF COURSE I HAVE. I HAVE FIVE SOV......

SSH! DON'T TELL HIM WHAT YOU'VE GOT! I'LL DEAL WIV HIM!

Annie let forth a stream of gutter language which left Hester and the coachman shaken. She finished off—

AN' IF YOU WON'T TAKE US, MISTER, THERE'S PLENTY OF OTHERS THAT WILL. MAKE UP YER MIND!

GET IN!

Three-quarters of an hour later, they were in Stepney.

I'M NOT GOING ANY FURTHER, MISS, AND THAT'S THAT! YOU OWE ME HALF A SOVEREIGN!

COO—THAT'S ROBBERY! YOU...

BE QUIET, ANNIE. DRIVER, IF I GIVE YOU A WHOLE SOVEREIGN, WILL YOU SELL ME THAT LANTERN?

The driver agreed, and soon Annie was leading Hester down a foul-smelling alley.

SMELLS A BIT, DON'T IT? BUT YOU GET USED TO IT.

YES, I EXPECT SO, ANNIE. BUT NOW I WANT TO SEE THOSE CHILDREN.

THERE'LL BE HEAPS UNDER HERE. FIGHT WE DO, FOR A PLACE HERE. HALF A MO' AND I'LL SHOW YOU.

DON'T WAKE 'EM, MISS! IT WOULDN'T BE KIND, YOU SEE. ASLEEP, THEY CAN FORGET ABOUT BEING HUNGRY.

THIS CAN'T BE TRUE!

But as night went on, and they moved from one pathetic sleeping place to another, anger replaced horror for Hester.

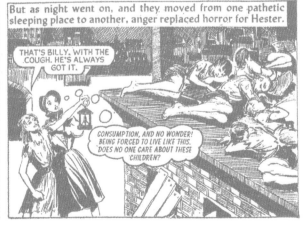

THAT'S BILLY, WITH THE COUGH. HE'S ALWAYS GOT IT.

CONSUMPTION, AND NO WONDER! BEING FORCED TO LIVE LIKE THIS. DOES NO ONE CARE ABOUT THESE CHILDREN?

After many weeks, and much hardship, the story reached its conclusion with the Langley family opening a home for the waifs and strays. As with almost all Bunty stories, the ending was a happy one, leaving the reader satisfied that all was well with the world.

# BUNTY'S CUT-OUT WARDROBE

This week Bunty shows off some pretty summer dresses, and also her riding and tennis outfits. Cut the clothes out round the thick black lines but be careful to leave on the tabs.
Look out for more clothes next week!

SLIP RACQUET UNDER LEFT ARM.

When the pop boom hit Britain in the early sixties, Bunty was quick to include stories with a modern music setting. The traditional themes weren't far away, though, and in this story from 1964 we meet a girl trying to save her grandfather from disaster, a mysterious 'organiser' called Madame Svengler and a title which certainly wouldn't be acceptable today.

# STELLA and the SWINGING FIVE

STELLA STARR, a young guitar player, had just joined the newly formed girls' beat group known as The Swinging Five. Though she sensed there was something odd about the group's organiser, a strange woman called Madame Svengler, Stella hoped to earn enough money to help save her old grandfather's run-down cafe. The Swinging Five, despite Stella's misgivings, were a smash hit at a local ballroom, and now they were to begin a nation-wide tour.

Next morning, Madame woke the girls early.

MEGAN! MEGAN! WAKE UP!

WE DIDN'T GET TO BED TILL AFTER MIDNIGHT—NO WONDER I'M STILL TIRED.

After a hasty breakfast—

HURRY UP, GIRLS! WE'VE GOT TO CATCH THE EARLY EXCURSION TRAIN. IT'S CHEAPER.

PHEW! WELL, WE CAUGHT THE TRAIN. MADAME'S TERRIBLY MEAN ABOUT MONEY, BUT THE GROUP SEEMS CERTAIN TO BE A SUCCESS, AFTER LAST NIGHT!

After a long, tiring journey—

GOLLY, I'LL BE GLAD TO GET TO OUR DIGS, AND RELAX FOR A BIT.

YES, I FEEL WORN OUT.

But Madame had other plans.

COME ALONG, GIRLS, I'VE ARRANGED A PRESS CONFERENCE.

I'VE HIRED A RECEPTION ROOM HERE FOR THE CONFERENCE—KEEP AWAY FROM REPORTERS AND LEAVE ALL THE TALKING TO ME!

I MIGHT HAVE KNOWN WE WOULDN'T BE STAYING HERE!

Some early Annual covers. These books were top of the Christmas list for lots of girls. The very earliest didn't have a date on the cover – but all featured the little Scottie dog which also appeared on the weekly cover until the mid seventies.

**BUNTY** THE BOOK FOR GIRLS

**BUNTY** The Book for Girls

**BUNTY** THE BOOK for GIRLS 1966

**BUNTY** The BOOK for GIRLS 1967

**BUNTY** The BOOK for GIRLS 196

**BUNTY** The BOOK for GIRLS 1970

**BUNTY** The BOOK for GIRLS 1972

★ A letter for Nancy—by " air mail "!★

# THE LAND OF NOWHERE

WHEN Nancy Wilson watered the sunflowers in her garden with a special growing powder, they just grew and grew. Then she climbed the sunflower forest to look for her cat, Prudence, and found herself in a strange new land—the Land of Nowhere. There, Nancy was given magical powers, but each time she used them, she landed in trouble—

24.12.83 BTY

24.12.83 BTY

**Nancy's first day at the Academy—NEXT WEEK.**

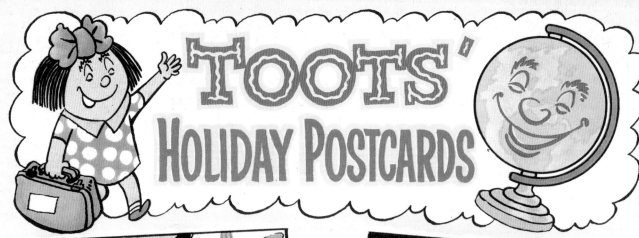

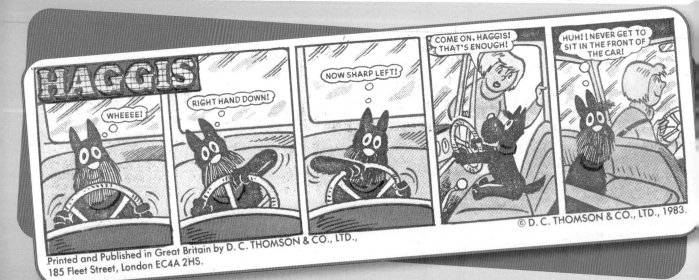

Printed and Published in Great Britain by D. C. THOMSON & CO., LTD., 185 Fleet Street, London EC4A 2HS.

# 'TOOTS' and HAGGIS

Printed and Published in Great Britain by D. C. THOMSON & CO., LTD.,
185 Fleet Street, London EC4A 2HS.

NEXT TUESDAY—The kidnappers come to school—to look for the Invisible Schoolgirl!

Although it would be true to say that almost every leading Bunty character was female, boys did make an appearance now and again – as these stories show.

## TOM FARMER WANTS A WIFE!

*Problems and laughter in 1983 when Carole Farmer sets out to find her absent-minded big brother the perfect wife.*

## MY BROTHER'S A POP STAR

*For Stella Jones, life with her pop star younger brother, Sonny Popkiss, was far from fun in 1974.*

## Donna and the DIAMONDS

*And in 1966 there was the girl who pretended to be a boy, in order to help her sick brother and his friends find fame.*

## BOY BLUE the ROCKIN' ROBOT

*More pop star fun from the seventies. This time we meet Janet Freeman who has to cope with a most unusual star – her brother's latest invention.*

When it wasn't showing off readers' school badges, the full colour back cover was often used for other 'educational' purposes. Among the topics featured were costumes from far-off lands, strange customs, world-wide dances, musical instruments, historical facts and strange methods of transport. Anything, in fact, that would interest the readers.

# Curious Carts

# COLOURFUL
# COSTUMES

Gaily-painted donkey-carts of the kind shown in this picture, are often seen in Sicily, largest of the Mediterranean islands.

This lovely girl from Japan is a striking figure in her gaily-coloured kimono. You will seldom see her without her bright parasol and fan.

# FARES, PLEASE!
## SOME OF THE UNUSUAL WAYS USED BY PEOPLE TO TRAVEL FROM PLACE TO PLACE IN OTHER COUNTRIES.

# WELL
# PLAYED!

Here you see a kind of horse-taxi that is used in Paris. It is very comfortable to ride in.

In Austria and Switzerland, the wire-stringed zither is a great favourite.

# See How They Dance

A Mexican caballero seeking a partner for the Hat Dance would be wise to choose a girl with dainty feet for in this Mexican dance the girl does some of the steps inside the brim of the man's sombrero.

# BEST OF LUCK

In Kennoway in Fife, there used to stand a tree covered in horseshoes. Legend had it that if a horse cast a shoe, your wish would be granted if you nailed it to the Wishing Tree.

# ROCK-A-BYE BABY

In Rumania, baby sleeps in a light basket-work cradle which is slung from the ceiling. The gaily-coloured blanket which covers it was woven at home by the proud mother.

# LADY CYCLISTS

The first-ever lady cyclists were seen in the streets of London in 1819. The machine they rode was known as a pedestrian hobby-horse. The rider pushed the bike along with her feet.

The back cover was also used to illustrate classic poems and songs. Turn over to see a beautifully illustrated adaptation of Longfellow's classic poem . . .

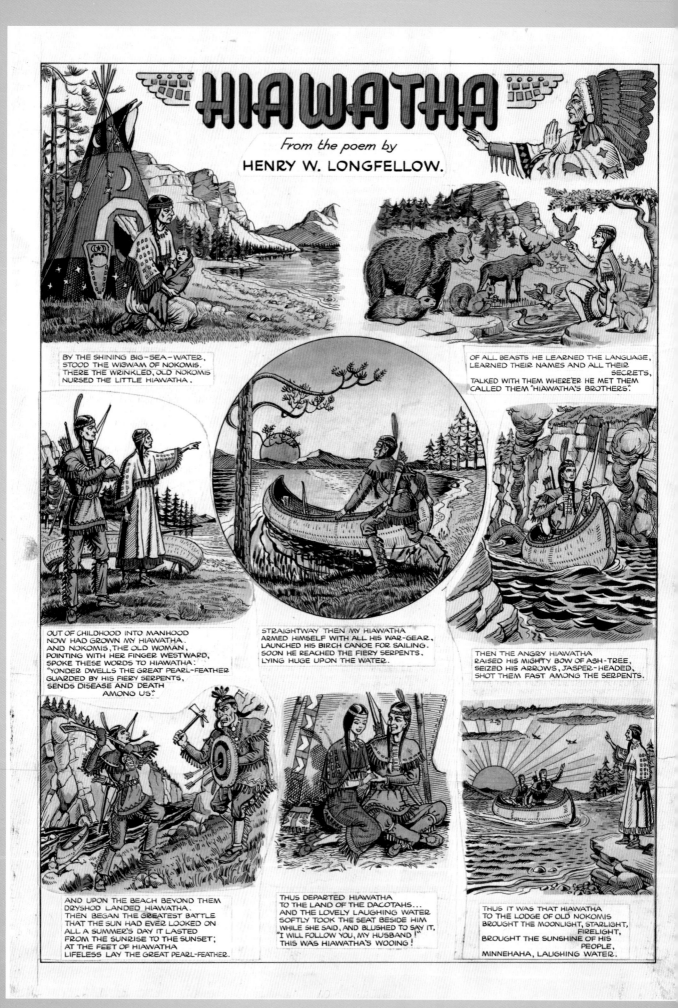

**Family life was very important to Bunty readers – and this cute and mischievous character was everyone's ideal little sister.**

*O*NE Easter, when my sister Mitsy was almost five, Mum took her along to the market when she went shopping. My name is Linda Crawford, by the way, and although Mitsy is a little scamp, she is very fond of animals and birds —and she fell in love with a fluffy little chicken!

# My Sister Mitsy

But Mitsy wasn't put off so easily.

MUM, I'D LOVE ONE OF THESE LITTLE CHICKS. CAN I HAVE ONE TO TAKE HOME WITH ME?

IT WOULDN'T BE FAIR TO THE CHICKEN, LOVE. IT WOULD DIE WITHOUT ITS MOTHER AND YOU WOULDN'T LIKE THAT, WOULD YOU?

LITTLE CHICKENS COME OUT OF EGGS, DON'T THEY, LINDA?

YES, MITSY— THAT'S RIGHT!

AND THE MOTHER HEN SITS ON THE EGGS. WELL—IN THAT CASE—

But nothing could have been further from the truth.

Mum sent for the doctor—

# '70s BUNTY

By the 1970s, Bunty's appearance had changed – and another change was just around the corner.

A summer sizzler.

The very last cover to feature the Scottie dog motif.

Pushchair pranks—but no Scottie dog to be seen.

No. 861–JULY 13, 1974.

EVERY TUESDAY

PRICE 4p

BATHING SHELTER

Beachwards Bunty makes her way,
She's out to get a tan today.

But look at this! That man's so fat!
The sun will never get past that!

Then a dog that's very wet,
Spoils the best spot she's found yet!

Next she's thumped by a wayward ball,
This is just no good at all!

What's this? Has Bunty had enough?
Has the going become too rough?

No. 875–OCTOBER 19, 1974.

EVERY TUESDAY

PRICE 4p

"I'm telling you, it's going to rain!"
Hear Bunty warn her pals in vain.

"You'll see! It will just pour!" says she,
"And dry back in our tent I'll be!"

Now rushing for cover at great speed,
Her pals wish they had paid her heed!

"I told you, -o!" hear Bunty crow
"My forecast's often right, you know!"

But here's a thin...
All shaken up ...
How her pals ...
Now Bunty's w...

No. 1027—September 17, 1977

EVERY TUESDAY

PRICE 7p

Young Mary Lou looks rather sad,
Being with Bunty can't be THAT bad!

Her niece thinks that it's MUCH more fun,
When Bunty breaks into a run!

But Bunty's heading for a fall,
As that pup dashes for its ball.

Regular story polls made sure Bunty editorial staff was aware of the kind of stories which were most popular with the readers. Staff also kept a close watch on changing trends and current interests, to make sure the stories kept up to date. But on many occasions Bunty was well ahead of the game when it came to ideas – as these three stories show.

Jamara tries to make herself invisible—but fails!

# ABRACADABRA ACADEMY

**J**AMARA JONES wanted to be an ordinary school-girl, but Jamara's mother was a witch and wanted her daughter to grow up to be a witch, too. So, in order that Jamara should learn all about spells and magic, she was sent to Abracadabra Academy, a school for witchcraft!

NOW I'LL JUST SHOW YOU A VERY SIMPLE FIRST YEAR SPELL! FOR THIS YOU NEED A GOOD BREW OF FISH-HEADS, APPLE-CORES AND DANDELION SEEDS.

OHHH, WHAT A BORE. I DO WANT TO BE A WITCH. W DO I HAVE TO LISTEN T THEIR DAFT SPELLS?

SAY WITH ME, GIRLS—BUBBLING POT OF MYSTIC STEW—CHANGE THE WELLINGTON TO A SHOE!

THERE! THE WE HAS BECOME SIMPLE LITTLE S EXPECT SOME O ALREADY DONE SCHOOL, B REMEMB

AND PEOPLE WONDER WHY I DON'T WANT TO BE A WITCH! IT'S DANGEROUS!

In 1978, long before we'd ever heard of Harry Potter and Hogwarts school, Bunty had its own trainee witch in the shape of Jamara Jones, who was a pupil at the memorably named ABRACADABRA ACADEMY. Unlike Harry, Jamara wasn't all that keen on magic and her spells invariably turned out badly — meaning lots of laughs for the readers.

**Della sets to work to make uniforms for the Japanese troops.**

# DETESTABLE DELLA

WHEN the Japanese invaded Malaya in 1942, the girls of St Monica's school were evacuated by air from the island of Sunvam. Della Mornay, the daughter of a British officer, stayed behind to help some mission—school girls for whom there was no room on the plane. Hiding in the jungle brought sickness to many of the girls, so Della persuaded the Japanese to round them up and put them in an internment camp where they could receive medical attention. For this, Della was branded a traitor.

The classic and very popular TV series of the 1980s, Tenko, was set in a women's prison camp in Singapore during World War 11. But several years previously, a similar Bunty story, set in a Malayan prison camp, had proved to be a great hit with readers. In this tale, a courageous schoolgirl made herself unpopular by appearing to side with the enemy while, all the time, she was actually helping her fellow prisoners and allies. Her name was Della Mornay — but she was better known as DETESTABLE DELLA.

# The SECRET LIFE of FENELLA FIELD

FENELLA FIELD lived in a smart area of Chelpond, and attended an expensive private school.

It could easily come straight out of a modern day soap opera — the girl who, on the death of her mother, discovers she had been adopted as a baby and sets out to get to know her birth family. Forced to keep her identity a secret, the young heroine becomes a lodger with her natural family while she waits for the ideal time to reveal the truth. This very up to date plot appeared in Bunty during 1973, and regular readers couldn't wait for the next instalment of The Secret Life of FENELLA FIELD.

*When it came to careers, none was more appealing to Bunty readers than nursing – and no nurse was more appealing than Katy O'Connor.*
*The bubbly Irish girl was a favourite for many years. Whether she was training at St Christopher's Hospital or working as a nurse on a cruise liner, Katy's cheerfulness and ready smile made her just the tonic for patients of all ages. Like several other Bunty characters, Katy began 'life' as a prose story, but proved so popular that she soon graduated to picture stories.*

*Now's your chance to enjoy an early medical adventure with Bunty's very own 'floating' angel.*

*This 1962 Annual story shows the Four Marys in full colour for the first time. Note that the girls are called by their full names, not the shortened nicknames that became the norm in later years.*

# The FOUR MARYS

THE Four Marys were all members of the Third Form at St Elmo's School for Girls, and shared the same study in Bee's House. It was a half-holiday and the girls were all planning to spend it in different ways. Mary Field was going to play hockey, Mary Radleigh meant to take things easy, Mary Cotter had a singing lesson, and Mary Simpson was going on an outing with the school's Sketching Club.

MISS PRINGELL, THE NEW ART MISTRESS, AND THE REST OF THE SKETCHING CLUB ARE IN THE QUAD. I MUSTN'T KEEP THEM WAITING!

I'LL SEE YOU LATER, GIRLS!

WE ARE GOING TO THE RUINS OF ELMBURY ABBEY, GIRLS. BY THE WAY, SKETCHES MADE TODAY MAY BE ENTERED FOR THE HELEN DAWSON PRIZE.

GOSH, I'D LOVE TO WIN THAT!

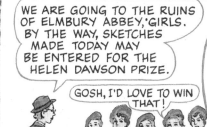

*The Helen Dawson Prize was an award presented to St Elmo's by an old pupil, now a very well known artist, and was competed for annually. It was usually won by one of the senior girls, and it would be a great honour for the Third Form if Mary gained the prize.*

Shortly afterwards—

THERE'S THE ABBEY IN THE DISTANCE. IT'S A LOVELY OLD PLACE!

OH HULLO, MARY. ANN FAIRLIE WAS IN ASKING FOR YOUR DRAWING FOR THE COMPETITION, SO I GAVE IT TO HER.

BUT **THIS** IS THE SKETCH I DID! OH DEAR— YOU'VE GIVEN ANN THE WRONG ONE! THE ONE YOU'VE GIVEN ANN WAS DRAWN BY A MAN I MET AT THE ABBEY!

Meanwhile, in the art room—

I'M QUITE SURE THIS ISN'T SIMPSON'S OWN WORK! I SHALL HAVE TO DEAL WITH HER SEVERELY FOR TRYING TO CHEAT!

The door opened, and Mary Simpson rushed into the room!

PLEASE, MA'AM MY FRIENDS GAVE YOU THE WRONG DRAWING. THAT SKETCH ON THE WALL ISN'T THE ONE I DID!

I KNOW IT ISN'T! THIS SKETCH IS THE WORK OF FENTON SLADE, THE WELL-KNOWN LANDSCAPE ARTIST.

THERE IS HIS HALLMARK. FENTON SLADE ALWAYS BRINGS A BUTTERFLY SOMEWHERE INTO HIS SKETCHES AND DRAWINGS.

LATER

IT GIVES ME GREAT PLEASURE TO PRESENT YOU WITH THE HELEN DAWSON PRIZE. YOUR OWN SKETCH WAS THE BEST OF THE ENTRIES, AND NOW THAT YOU HAVE HAD A LESSON FROM FENTON SLADE YOU SHOULD GO ON TO GREATER THINGS.

THE END

*The Four Marys may have been the most popular school story over the years, but it was far from being the only story set in the classroom. Here are a few classics to jog your memory.*

Angela pays a secret visit to Greenwoods School!

# INNOCENT ANGELA

LOVELY, innocent-looking Angela Seymour was a new pupil at Wynminster School. But no one guessed that Angela had been purposely "planted" at Wynminster by her aunt and uncle at Greenwoods School, Wynminster's rivals. On her first night, Angela stole the keys from the Head's study.

**A girl plots to destroy the reputation of a top boarding school.**

ALL I'VE GOT TO DO NOW, IS TAKE THESE KEYS TO UNCLE GEORGE AND AUNT EMILY AT GREEN WOODS AND FIND OUT WHAT ELSE THEY WANT ME TO DO.

AH! GOOD TO SEE YOU AGAIN, ANGELA. HAVE YOU GOT THE KEYS?

★ *Deanna sends an important message to the outside world.* ★

## The SCHOOL BENEATH THE DOME

ONE morning, the pupils of Marlborough Girls' High awakened to find themselves prisoners in a transparent dome. Phobos and Deimos, two strange women from space, had come to Earth to find out how children were taught and what they were taught. Deanna Darwin, captain of the Fifth Form, was determined to thwart the space-women, but, as a punishment, she had been surrounded by a powerful magnetic field, so that she was unable to touch anything and could not eat. However, the space-women were unaware that the magnetic field was growing weaker and that Deanna was just pretending that nothing had changed. One day, some of the girls began acting most strangely—

WHEE! LOOK AT ME—I'M A TWO-HEADED MONSTER FROM MARS!

HEY—LOOK, DEANNA—I'VE GOT A MAGNETIC FIELD, TOO! THE TROUBLE IS I DON'T KNOW IF I'M A NORTH POLE OR A SOUTH POLE—OR JUST UP-THE-POLE! I'LL TOUCH YOU AND SEE WHAT HAPPENS.

Deanna found herself

Meanwhile, the space-women were also puzzled.

**Strange happenings in 1966 when an entire school is 'kidnapped'.**

# MARSHA  THE PERFECT SCHOOLGIRL

MARSHA ZENON, a new girl at Plunkett Academy, was no ordinary girl. She had been sent from outer space to study the people of Earth. At first, Marsha, whose knowledge was encyclopaedic, was unpopular because she was too good, but as she grew more tactful the girls had warmed to her. One day, during a gym lesson—

WELL DONE, BEA. COME ALONG, MARSHA.

**A girl from outer space visits Earth on a spying mission.**

**And we mustn't forget** inky. In 1975, 'the dog with a mind of his own' found himself employed as watchdog at St Ives School for Girls.

*Over the years, skating features and stories about skating were popular inclusions. This Annual feature from 1964 highlighted Olympic champions on the ice.*

# The CREAM of the ICE

## A PAGE OF OLYMPIC SKATING STARS

**1908. MADGE SYERS, GREAT BRITAIN.**

Ice figure skating was first included in the Olympic Games in 1908, and Madge became the first-ever woman to win the coveted gold medal.

**1920. M. JULIENNE, SWEDEN.**

In 1920, the gold medal went for the first time to one of the homes of winter sports, when this Swedish skater was the victor.

**1924. HERMA PLANK, AUSTRIA.**

**1960. CAROL HEISS, U.S.A.**

**1928-32-36. SONJA HENIE, NORWAY.**

Besides winning the Olympic Gold Medal, Herma Plank was five times world champion, and she is the only skater to have won a world title in both solo and pairs events.

Beautiful Carol Heiss kept the Olympic title in U.S.A. when she won in 1960. After her success, she, like Sonja Henie, entered films.

The brilliant Sonja was only 14 when she won the first of her three gold medals. She turned professional and made a success in films.

**1948. BARBARA ANN SCOTT, CANADA.**

**1952, JEANETTE ALTWEGG, GREAT BRITAIN**

**1956. TENLEY ALBRIGHT, U.S.A.**

In the first Olympic Games after the last war, held in London, Barbara Ann thrilled Europe with an exciting new style of free-skating developed in America.

Jeanette was the second woman from Great Britain to win this event and her magnificent achievement was later honoured by her country when she had the M.B.E. conferred upon her.

Second to Jeanette Altwegg by less than three points in the 1952 Olympics was Tenley Albright. But her day came in 1956 when she became the first American to win the title.

# THE DANCING DONNELLYS

Tell your mates about all the good things in "Bunty."

NEXT WEEK — Jane comes to a decision.

While Moira Kent was the first ballet dancer to grace the pages of Bunty, she was certainly not the last. It wasn't long before Moira was joined by countless other young dancers – each with her own story to tell. Here are just a few who have danced through the pages of Bunty over the years.

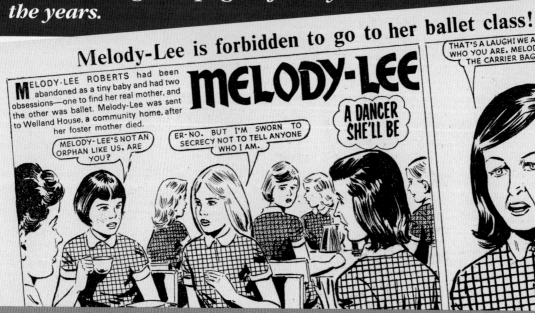

Abandoned as a baby, 'guttersnipe' Melody-Lee had two dreams in life – to find her mother and to become a ballet dancer. The stories followed her as she struggled against the odds, in an effort to achieve her ultimate desire.

Margot Bennett was the envy of many readers. The Bennetts had their very own ballet company and young Margot appeared in towns and villages all over the country – often performing in front of celebrities and royalty.

Madame Petrov, a renowned ballet teacher, had many stories to tell about the lucky girls who had passed through her school on their way to stardom. This story told of Fiona, a girl with a very special talent and a very kind heart.

## The DANCER from THE ISLES

MADAME GRETA PETROV, the famous ballet teacher, sat in her office. Her assistant, Elma Harper, looked on as the pages of an old photograph album flicked over to disclose pictures of girls—all pupils of Madame Petrov, some now great names in ballet. Then, amidst all the budding Fonteyns and Pavlovas, there appeared a photograph of a castle . . . .

APPIN CASTLE HOTEL, ON THE ISLAND OF STROMNAY ....... DO YOU REMEMBER OUR HOLIDAY THERE, ELMA— AND THE STRANGE THINGS THAT HAPPENED AFTERWARDS?

SCOTLAND ON OK

★ Jessie plays a trick on the ballet pupils. ★

## BACKSTREET BALLERINA

BARBARA TAYLOR gave ballet lessons in the East End of London, using a converted stable as a school. Recently she had accepted as a pupil an aggressive, undisciplined girl—Jessie Tandy—who was in danger of being sent to an approved school because of her bad behaviour. Jessie loved to dance and Barbara hoped that the ballet discipline might help her. The other girls, out of affection for Barbara, accepted Jessie during class, but did not want to be friendly with her outside because their parents had forbidden it. Hurt and angry, Jessie went off after saying she would be back to make the girls sorry. The next evening—

A few minutes later—

GIRLS! IS THIS SOME SORT OF A JOKE?

IT DOESN'T LOOK AS THOUGH JESSIE IS COMING THIS EVENING AFTER ALL, BARBARA.

NO, MISS. OOOH, OH! MY BACK ITCHES! OOOH!

PERHAPS SO... RIGHT, GIRLS... LONGER. T...

WHAT DO YOU KNOW ABOUT THIS, JESSIE?

Barbara told the girls to change and go ho...

IT MUST HAVE BEEN HER. S... LOOKS PLEASED WITH HERSE... WE'LL GET YOU FOR THIS, JESSIE TANDY!

YOU ASKED FOR TROUBLE AND YOU GOT IT. IT WAS EASY TO GET IN THROUGH THE SKYLIGHT AND ... THE POWDER...

QUITE A BIT, I'D SAY. LOOK AT THIS, BARBARA! AN EMPTY CARTON OF ITCHING POWDER FROM THAT JOKE SHOP ON BESSEY STREET.

I WAS SORRY FOR YOU, JESSIE, BUT NOT ANY MORE. IT'S NOT THE GIRLS' FAULT THEIR PARENTS WON'T LET THEM GO AROUND WITH YOU. IT'S YOUR FAULT!

YOU'RE A... I THOU... NICE, BU... I...

After a family tragedy, young Barbara Taylor gave up her dreams of becoming a famous dancer and, instead, opened a ballet school in the roughest part of London. There she hoped to help poor children share her love of dancing.

And then there was the girl who was destined to become even more popular than Moira Kent. The one and only...
*Lorna Drake*

★ A bunch of flowers melts Thelma Mayne's heart ★

## LORNA DRAKE

### ON THE LONELY ROAD OF A BALLERINA

LORNA DRAKE'S big day had come. A pupil at Thelma Mayne's ballet school, she had been asked to perform at a Charity Matinée, alongside some of the famous dancers of British ballet.

Only two things spoiled Lorna's happiness. Firstly, her father had recently undergone a serious eye operation, and Lorna didn't know if he would ever be able to see again. Secondly, Lorna wished that her father and Thelma Mayne could be friends. They had danced together in ballet until a stage accident ended Miss Mayne's career. She blamed Lorna's father for the accident, and never forgave him.

IMPERIAL BALLET THEATRE

THE CROWDS ARE GOING IN ALREADY. OH, I'M SO NERVOUS.

I'LL TAKE A LOOK BACKSTAGE WHILE DORIS HELPS YOU TO GET READY.

THESE FLOWERS HAVE ARRIVED FOR LORNA DRAKE.

OH? I'LL TAKE THEM TO HER.

*Lorna, a pupil of the incredibly strict – but fair – Thelma Mayne, starred in Bunty for many years and was a favourite with readers for several decades.*

# LORNA DRAKE

## AND THE CHINA BALLERINA

LORNA DRAKE, a promising young dancer, was being trained by Thelma Mayne, whose own brilliant ballet career had been brought to an end by an accident which left her with a limp. Lorna had to work hard to attain the high standard set by Miss Mayne, but she thoroughly enjoyed every minute of her ballet lessons. She also attended the local council school, to receive a normal education. One morning—

THELMA MAYNE

I'VE ENTERED YOUR NAME FOR THE "DAILY CLARION" BALLET CONTEST, LORNA. THERE IS A SILVER MEDAL FOR THE WINNER AND A FIFTY POUND AWARD FOR HER BALLET TEACHER.

But as Lorna was leaving the room—

I DON'T WANT LORNA TO KNOW THIS, DORIS, BUT WE BADLY NEED THAT FIFTY POUNDS. THERE HAVE BEEN SO MANY BILLS LATELY THAT I'M HAVING A STRUGGLE TO MANAGE.

OH! NOW I'VE GOT TO WIN THE CONTEST, TO HELP MISS MAYNE!

Lorna practised hard in every spare moment.

Two hours later –

PHEW! I'M TIRED! MISS MAYNE THINKS I'VE GONE TO THE LIBRARY TO DO SOME SCHOOL WORK. I'LL HAVE TO THINK OF ANOTHER EXCUSE TOMORROW.

GET A MOVE ON THERE – WE DON'T HAVE ALL DAY TO WASTE!

When Lorna got home, she was tired and stiff.

FOR THE FIRST TIME IN MY LIFE, I DON'T FEEL LIKE DANCING. BUT I HAVE A PRACTICE WITH MISS MAYNE NOW.

COME ON, LORNA – THIS WON'T DO! YOU'RE DANCING SLUGGISHLY.

The next few days dragged wearily for Lorna.

SCRUBBING AND DANCING AND CLEANING – I CAN'T GO ON LIKE THIS! BUT THERE'S NO WAY OUT.

LORNA HAS LOST ALL INTEREST IN THE "CLARION" CONTEST, DORIS. SHE MAKES EXCUSES TO STAY OUT AFTER SCHOOL, AND ALL THE SPARKLE HAS GONE FROM HER DANCING.

IF ONLY I COULD EXPLAIN TO HER!

One evening, as Lorna went to the store –

OH, DEAR – THERE'S AGGIE. I MUSTN'T LET HER SEE ME.

But it was too late. Lorna's school friend, Aggie, had already seen her.

HELLO, LORNA! I'VE COME TO MEET MY COUSIN BETH, FROM WORK. SHE'S ON THE HAT COUNTER IN THE STORE.

As Beth joined Aggie, Lorna slipped away.

HI, BETH! DID YOU SEE THE GIRL I WAS TALKING TO? THAT'S MY BEST FRIEND, LORNA DRAKE?

YOUR BEST FRIEND? WELL, THERE'S SOMETHI SHOULD TELL YOU. MR POWELL PLAYED A NAS TRICK ON YOUR FRIEND. I SAW IT ALL IN TH MIRROR AT THE HAT COUNTER BUT I DIDN'T DA SAY ANYTHING IN CASE HE GAVE ME THE SACK

HE SMASHED A CHINA BALLERINA AND PUT THE BLAME ON LORNA. NOW SHE IS WORKING AS A CLEANER HERE TO PAY FOR THE DAMAGE.

COME ON, BETH! WE'RE GOING TO TELL MISS MAYNE ABOUT THIS. SHE HAS AN AWFUL TEMPER. I WOULDN'T LIKE TO BE IN MR POWELL'S SHOES!

MISS MAYNE – MAY WE SPEAK TO YOU, PLEASE? IT'S ABOUT LORNA.

ABOUT LORNA? OF COURSE. COME IN, BOTH OF YOU.

And half an hour later—

LORNA—COME WITH ME AT ONCE!

MISS MAYNE!

COME, LORNA! YOU'LL HAVE NO MORE TROUBLE WITH MR POWELL!

SHE'S BEATEN US, RITA. IT WOULD RUIN US IF THE PAPERS GOT THE STORY.

Thelma Mayne gave Mr Powell a piece of her mind.

I KNOW THE TRUTH ABOUT THIS WHOLE BUSINESS, YOU NASTY LITTLE MAN. YOUR DAUGHTER HAS ENTERED FOR THE "CLARION" CONTEST, HASN'T SHE? SO YOU BROKE THAT CHINA FIGURE YOURSELF, AND TRICKED LORNA INTO THINKING SHE WAS TO BLAME! ADMIT IT, OR I'LL GO TO THE EDITOR OF THE LOCAL NEWSPAPER WITH MY STORY—AND I HAVE A WITNESS!

NO, NO, DON'T DO THAT! I ADMIT IT ALL—I APOLOGISE.

A few days later, after a good rest, Lorna was dancing on top form again.

IT GIVES ME GREAT PLEASURE TO PRESENT THE "CLARION" SILVER MEDAL TO MISS LORNA DRAKE, AND THE CHEQUE TO HER TEACHER, MISS MAYNE.

TO THINK THAT MY CHANCES WERE ALMOST RUINED, AND ALL BECAUSE OF A LITTLE CHINA BALLERINA.

# BUNTY'S
## CUT-OUT WARDROBE

THE SNOW MAIDEN

COPPELIA

GISELLE

FIREBIRD

THIS week Bunty wears costumes from some of the best-known ballets. Cut round the thick, black lines—being careful to leave on the tabs—and fit the costumes to the figure.

SWAN LAKE

ROYAL BALLET SCHOOL PRACTICE COSTUME

Orphans and orphanages featured in many Bunty stories and, although they were often tear-jerking tales of hardship and loneliness, this wasn't always the case. Often the stories featured heroines who were happy in their home and who took it upon themselves to look after the younger children who were in care. One such girl was Angela Winters — better known as...

That afternoon, Nurse Reid, the most unpopular nurse on the staff, came back on duty, and supervised the final tidy-up of the children before the visitors arrived.

Cindy watched as Stella strode across the hall towards Mrs Bradley.

# BUNTY CLUB CORNER

**CALLING ALL CLUB MEMBERS! THIS PAGE OF COMPETITIONS IS SPECIALLY FOR YOU—AND FORTY PRIZES MUST BE WON!**

CXOZK GRR EUAX GTYCKXY OT IUJK

## WHO IS HE?

This singer is the leader of a very popular group. Beautiful bracelet and pendant sets are waiting for the ten club members who send in the neatest postcards giving his name.

## HOW MANY Bs?

HOW MANY THINGS IN THIS PICTURE BEGIN WITH THE LETTER B? POODLE BROOCHES WILL BE AWARDED TO THE 10 READERS WHO SEND IN THE BEST LISTS.

## QUICK CROSSWORD

Dainty manicure sets will be awarded to the 10 club members who submit the neatest solutions to this crossword puzzle.

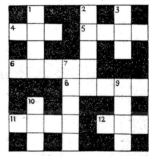

ACROSS: 4 Peas grow in this. 5 Boy's name. 6 Large box. 8 Command. 11 Dull colour. 12 United States of America.
DOWN: 1 Two plus two. 2 Important liquid. 3 A tin. 7 The Olympic Games were held here. 9 Comfort. 10 Anger.

## SPOT THE MISTAKES

Can you spot the ten deliberate mistakes our artist has made in this picture? The 10 club members who send in the neatest postcards will win lovely pen and pencil sets.

ALL ANSWERS IN THE BUNTY SECRET CODE, AND ON POSTCARDS PLEASE, TO—

**CLUB CORNER (12), "BUNTY," 12 FETTER LANE, FLEET STREET, LONDON, E.C.4.**

NOTE—The Editor will judge these competitions. Neatness will count and his decision will be final.

## HOW TO JOIN The Bunty Club

1—Buy a postal order for 2s. Make it payable to BUNTY at LONDON Post Office by writing these words on the space provided and cross it with two heavy ink lines /& Co./. (Your parents will tell you if you have done it properly.)
2—Cut out and fill in both sections of the attached form in BLOCK LETTERS. Please use a ball-point pen or sharp pencil.
3—Send the completed form and postal order to:—
BUNTY CLUB, "BUNTY," P.O. BOX 72, 186 FLEET STREET, LONDON, E.C.4.
Stamp your envelope with a 3d stamp.
You will be sent your membership card with the club's secret code, secret mark and the beautiful chromium and enamel badge of the Bunty "Scottie."

### BUNTY CLUB MEMBERSHIP FORM

I enclose a 2/- Postal Order No. ...............................

My FULL NAME is ...................................................

HOUSE No. and STREET ...........................................

TOWN and COUNTY ...............................................

#### FILL IN THIS POSTAL LABEL ALSO

Miss ...................................................................

House No. and Street ..............................................

Town ..................................................................

County .................................................................

SPECIAL
25th
BIRTHDAY
NUMBER

**FREE** *Inside* **A SUPER SURPRISE GIFT**

# BUNTY

No. 1305—JANUARY 15, 1983.
EVERY TUESDAY

**14p**
IR 21p
(INC. V.A.T.)

## 25 YEARS OF FAVOURITE READING FOR GIRLS

SPECIAL
25th
BIRTHDAY
NUMBER

## WENDY THE TENNIS WONDER

A girl's struggle to become a tennis star.

**1959**

## HUMPY DUMPY

The hilarious adventures of Flora MacVicar, and her pet from the depths of Loch Ness.

**1965**

## FAME AT HER FINGERTIPS

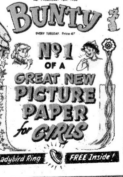

**1961**

The trials and tribulations of a budding concert pianist.

**1963**

## PADDY LONG LEGS

She was a terror on stilts!

# SQUARE PEG

**1968**

**1969**

The funny tale of a tomboy at a snobbish girls' school.

## A BED CALLED FRED

A girl's epic journey from John O' Groats to Land's End— pushing a four-poster bed.

## BRONCHO BUTTERCUP

**1970**

The comical tale of a cow that believes it is a show-jumper.

### *"IT'S A DOG'S LIFE!"* says Inky

**1972**

The funny adventures of a lovable dog—told by the dog itself!

Patsy Hanley is table-tennis mad—and determined to be a champion.

**1971**

## PING PONG PATSY

**1973**

An entire ballet school is abducted —in mysterious floating bubbles!

*The Bubble Ballerinas*

## CATCH THE CAT

**1976**

The daring adventures of a mystery girl in World War II.

## The TAMING of TERESA

**1978**

The amazing story of Teresa, who was brought up by a pack of wolves.

## *HANNAH in the HOUSE of DOLLS*

**1980**

**1979**

A thrilling war story.

## DON'T CRY FOR ME!

Thrills and danger when deadly dolls come alive!

BTY 15.1.83  2

### ★ From '58 to '83 Toots is always fun to see! ★

Bunty Library No. 237—"I Must Find My Mum!"—On Sale NOW.

Animal stories came in all shapes and sizes. The stories shown here all appeared in weekly or annual publications during the sixties and seventies – and some of the titles are certainly memorable.

# Lindy Martin
## The Animals' Friend

LINDY MARTIN MUST **NOT** GO!

KEEP LINDY MARTIN

# Hetty's HAPPY HIPPO

PUBLIC HALL
GRAND PET SHOW
JUDGING 2 p.m. Saturday

**W**HEN Hetty Bright found a baby hippopotamus, her family reluctantly agreed to give him a home in the back garden—until his owners turned up. But they didn't turn up and Hippy became just like any other household pet—only much loved.

A PET SHOW! I'LL ENTER YOU FOR IT, HIPPY! EVERYBODY WILL SOON SEE HOW CLEVER AND NICE YOU ARE. YOU'RE BOUND TO WIN!

# BARBARA'S BABY ELEPHANT

I REALLY CAN'T IMAGINE WHAT PERSUADED YOU TO ALLOW BARBARA TO KEEP THAT ELEPHANT. IT MUST CAUSE A LOT OF TROUBLE AND DAMAGE AROUND THE PLACE.

AUNT MOIRA DOESN'T LIKE POOR TUSKER. I JUST HOPE SHE DOESN'T TURN MUM AGAINST HIM.

**B**ARBARA WALLACE kept a most unusual pet at her home, Oak Farm. This was Tusker, a baby Siamese elephant. Tusker had taken to his new life very well, although some visitors to the farm found this hard to believe.

Quackers loves crackers!

MAISIE MOSS had a pet duck, Quackers, and he soon turned into quite a character. On the strength of his personality Quackers was soon in demand for advertisements.

GOOD NEWS, QUACKERS. YOU'VE LANDED ANOTHER JOB—ADVERTISING CRISP'S CRACKERS!

QUA-ACCK!

DON'T FORGET YOUR PIANO PRACTICE, MAISIE!

OH-ER-ALL RIGHT, MUM! I HAVE TO TAKE QUACKERS TO THE STUDIO FIRST, THOUGH.

YOU AND THAT DUCK! MIND YOU PRACTISE FOR TWO HOURS WHEN YOU COME HOME!

WASTE OF TIME! IT'S YOUR CAREER I WANT TO WORK AT, QUACKERS.

IF CRISP'S SELL MORE CRACKERS BECAUSE OF YOU, YOU'LL BE OFFERED LOTS MORE ADVERTISING WORK.

QUARRK! QUARRK!

At the Film Studio—

I'M MAISIE MOSS. I'VE BROUGHT MY DUCK FOR THE PHOTOGRAPHIC SESSION.

A DUCK? NOBODY TOLD ME ABOUT THIS.

I'M SORRY. THEY DEFINITELY BOOKED A DUCK. I THOUGHT IT WAS ALL ARRANGED.

I'LL EXPLAIN, MISS SHUTTER!

YOU SEE, THE ADVERTISING SLOGAN IS QUACKERS LOVES CRISP'S CRACKERS! IT RHYMES, YOU SEE.

YOU CORNY COPYWRITERS! OH, WELL—MY PHOTOGRAPHY WILL SAVE THE ADVERTISEMENT.

I BEG YOUR PARDON! A PHOTOGRAPH IS NOTHING WITHOUT A SNAPPY CAPTION.

YOU CALL THAT SNAPPY? I COULD THINK UP SOMETHING BETTER MYSELF!

KWARRRRK!

DO YOU MIND? QUACKERS DOESN'T LIKE LOUD ANGRY VOICES. HE'S GONE INTO THE CUPBOARD!

OH, SORRY. WELL, LET'S GET STARTED.

*More exciting adventures with Maisie and the amazing Quackers — NEXT WEEK.*

The only thing better than Bunty, was Bunty with a free gift. Jewellery was a popular option – as were booklets and transfers. Later gifts included the more modern stickers and sweets. Here are a few which proved successful with Bunty readers of all ages.

Souvenir Book of the Famous 'BUNTY' Picture Story

The GIRL OF THE ISLANDS

Presented FREE with "BUNTY"

The BiG BiRTHDAY BOOK

Happy Birthday !!

TIP·TOP·KNOTS Presented FREE with BUNTY

Presented with "BUNTY"

*Fashion wasn't much in evidence in the early years – except in features like this. Which style would you choose?*

# THEIR CROWNING GLORY
## HAIR STYLES of LONG AGO

Fresh flowers in the hair were a feature of many Spanish hairstyles. Of course, every girl had her attractive lace mantilla for special occasions.

In ancient Egypt, beads, combs and other ornaments were used to decorate the hair. Some of these elaborate styles must have taken hours to fix in place.

This style was popular at the beginning of the nineteenth century in France. The hair was partly pleated and tied up with braid.

This Dutch girl's hairstyle couldn't have been simpler. Her hair was pulled straight back from the face and caught up in a bun. Younger girls wore their hair in plaits.

This hairstyle is still fashionable in Japan, even though it originated hundreds of years ago. The hair is piled high on the head and fastened with combs or pins, decorated perhaps with flowers.

Red Indian maidens wore their long hair in a middle parting, and the two strands were tied with ribbons — a simple but becoming style.

In ancient Rome, women decorated their sleek hairstyles with rows of beads, or filmy veils attached to the crown of the head.

There's not much hair to be seen here. Greek women of old covered their hair with small round caps and head-scarves, which were draped over the head and shoulders.

*In the days when beauty contests were seen as the ultimate in glamour and sophistication, young Alice Taylor had big plans for her tomboy older sister.*

On her way home, Alice called at the garage where Sarah worked and told her the news.

IT ONLY GIVES US A WEEK, SARAH. BUT LOOK AT THIS—ISN'T IT FABULOUS? YOU'LL REALLY CATCH THE JUDGE'S EYE WEARING THIS.

I'LL CATCH PNEUMONIA, TOO! THAT LOOKS LIKE THE STRAP—WHERE'S THE REST OF IT?

IT'S ALL HERE, SARAH. IT STRETCHES TO YOUR EXACT SHAPE. I CAN JUST IMAGINE THE JUDGES CATCHING THEIR BREATH AS YOU GLIDE BY AND—

FALL FLAT ON MY FACE! COME OFF THAT DREAM CLOUD, ALICE! I AIN'T WEARING THAT POCKET HANDKERCHIEF, AND THAT'S THAT!

However, after a hearty meal of fish and chips, Sarah's temper was somewhat improved.

OKAY, SIS—LET'S BEGIN THE AGONY. WHERE DO WE START FIRST—WITH THE FALSE EYELASHES?

OH, NO, YOU DON'T NEED THOSE. FIRST, YOU MUST LEARN TO WALK AND SIT NICELY. GOODNESS KNOWS WHAT YOU'RE DOING TO YOUR SPINE, SITTING LIKE THAT!

IF YOU'RE SLOPPY IN YOUR WALK, UNTIDY IN YOUR APPEARANCE, THEN OTHERS WILL JUDGE YOU AT THE LOW VALUE YOU PLACE UPON YOURSELF. YOU MUST LEARN TO WALK LIKE A LADY, SARAH. NOW YOU TRY THIS SIMPLE TRICK—

COO! LOOK AT MISS PRIM AND PROPER!

THAT'S GOOD, SARAH—HEAD UP, LOOK STRAIGHT AHEAD. WHILE YOU'RE DOING THAT, TRY IMPROVING YOUR SPEECH AT THE SAME TIME, REPEAT THIS AFTER ME —HOW NOW BROWN COW...

—DON'T, SARAH! REMEMBER THE GOLDEN RULE—NEVER LOSE YOUR TEMPER. TRY COUNTING TO TEN AND YOUR ANGER WILL PASS.

HOW...NOW...BROWN—AAGH! YOU ROTTEN BRATS—I'LL FLAY YOU!

*This exceptionally popular story, which ran for 19 weeks in the mid sixties, proved to be just as big a favourite when reprinted in the following decade.*

The next morning—

YOUR BREAKFAST IS READY, SARAH—OH, SARAH, AREN'T YOU GOING TO TIDY UP FIRST?

NO! I'M TOO HUNGRY!

UGH! WHATEVER'S THIS? WHO'S PINCHED MY EGGS AND BACON?

NO MORE BACON AND EGGS FOR YOU, SARAH. YOU'VE GOT TO WATCH YOUR FIGURE. IT'S GRAPEFRUIT AND BLACK MOLASSES FROM NOW ON.

SO THAT'S YOUR ROTTEN GAME, IS IT? I GO ON A DIET SO YOU CAN SCOFF MY BACON! PROPER LITTLE PORKY, AREN'T YOU?

OH, SARAH, YOU KNOW THAT ISN'T TRUE. EATING THE RIGHT FOOD IS VERY IMPORTANT, AND GRAPEFRUIT IS GOOD FOR THE FIGURE.

IS IT? THEN YOU HAVE IT— YOU NEED IT MORE THAN ME! AND WHERE'S MY COFFEE? SOME ROTTER'S LEFT DIRTY DISH WATER IN MY CUP.

THAT'S NOT DISH WATER, IT'S HERB TEA—ONE OF THE FINEST THINGS FOR THE FIGURE.

I KNOW THIS IS HARD FOR YOU, SARAH, BUT PLEASE BE PATIENT WITH ME. YOU'LL THINK IT ALL WORTH-WHILE WHEN YOU WALK AWAY WITH THE BEAUTY CONTEST.

.HUH! AT THIS RATE YOU'LL HAVE TO CARRY ME THERE. I'LL BE TOO WEAK TO WALK!

That afternoon—

YOU KNOW, YOU'VE A BEAUTIFUL FACE, SARAH. IT'S A JOY FOR ME TO MAKE YOU UP AFTER SOME OF THE OLD WOMEN I HAVE TO HANDLE. THIS MAKE-UP WILL ADD A LOVELY VIVACITY TO YOUR NATURAL BEAUTY.

PAH! YOU CAN'T KID ME! I AIN'T EVER BEEN BEAUTIFUL.

BEING BEAUTIFUL IS LARGELY A MATTER OF FEELING BEAUTIFUL. WHEN I'VE CONVINCED YOU OF THIS, YOU'LL BE ABLE TO CONVINCE OTHERS, SARAH. NOW BRUSH YOUR HAIR—A HUNDRED STROKES SHOULD DO.

A HUNDRED STROKES! I'LL BE WORN OUT. ARE YOU SURE THERE AIN'T AN EASIER WAY TO BE BEAUTIFUL?

NOW SLIP INTO THIS SUIT— OH, DON'T SCOWL, SARAH! FROWNS AND RIGID LIPS RUIN YOUR FACE—KEEP THE CORNERS OF YOUR LIPS UP, EVEN WHEN YOU'RE SERIOUS.

COO! WHAT A LIFE! I'D RATHER LOOK MISERABLE AND ENJOY IT.

OH, DEAR, JUST LOOK AT YOUR HANDS, SARAH! THEY RUIN EVERYTHING! THEY'RE INGRAINED WITH GRIME AND GREASE.

SO! MECHANICS DON'T USUALLY HAVE LILY-WHITE HANDS! AND DON'T ASK ME TO GIVE UP MY JOB. I'M CRAZY ABOUT CARS AND ONE DAY I'LL HAVE MY OWN.

An hour later—

OH, WHAT A TRANSFORMATION! SOMEHOW I MUST GIVE YOU CONFIDENCE IN YOURSELF—I KNOW! WE'LL GO FOR A WALK IN THE PARK AND YOU'LL SEE JUST HOW MANY PEOPLE WILL STOP TO ADMIRE YOU.

HEAD HIGH, SARAH, AND LOOK AS IF YOU KNOW YOU'RE BEAUTIFUL AND ARE PROUD OF IT...OH, THAT'S VERY GOOD!

SHE'S DOING BETTER THAN I EVER DARED TO HOPE. NOW I'LL TAKE HER PAST THE FACTORIES. THE WORKERS WON'T KNOW WHAT'S HIT THEM WHEN THEY SEE HER.

WOW! WHAT A BEAUTY!

WHATEVER'S A LADY LIKE HER DOING ROUND HERE?

Suddenly—

OW! ME ROTTEN SHOE'S CAUGHT IN THE STUPID DRAIN! WHAT ARE YOU STARIN' AT, YOU NOSEY LOT? BUZZ OFF, BEFORE I BELT YOU ONE!

OH, NO! WILL I EVER CHANGE SARAH? IS IT POSSIBLE THAT I COULD MAKE HER MISS WORLD?

All eight judges came to their decision in record time— and Sarah was their choice.

ALL MY DREAMS HAVE COME TRUE AT LAST!

Several weeks later.

ADA

# WHAT YOUR

CHLOE - fresh
CHRISTINE - fair
CLARA - shining
CLARISSA - famous
CLAUDIA - lame
CLEO - famed
COLETTE - victorious
COLEEN - girl
CONSTANCE - constant
   maiden
   AL - fair
   A - goddess

DAISY - "the day's eye"
DALE - valley dweller
DARLENE - beloved
DAVINA - loved
DAWN - break of day
DEANNA - pure
DEBORAH - bee
DEIRDRE - sorrow
DELLA - noble
DENISE - goddess
DOLLY - God's gift
DOROTHY - gift of God

ABIGAIL - f
ADA - orna
ADELE - no
ADORA - be
ADRIENNE
AGATHA - g
AGNES - pu
AILEEN - lig
ALBERTA - n
ALEXANDRA
ALICE - truth
ALMA - kindly
ALTHEA - hea
ALVA - fair
AMANDA - lov
AMY - beloved
ANGELA - ang
ANITA - gracefu
ANNE - gracefu
ANTHEA - flowe
AUDREY - stron
AVIS - bird
BARBARA - mys

ANGELA

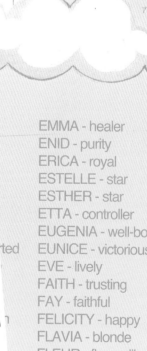

This free book from the sixties gives a real taste of its time. The bright, cheerful cover was certainly appealing and the name feature shown here was just one of many interesting pages for readers to enjoy. There was also a 'personal details' page for the girls to fill in. It asked for vital information – such as glove size and stocking size! Yes, changed days indeed.

*
THE BOOK OF
ME
and
MY
FRIENDS

EMMA - healer
ENID - purity
ERICA - royal
ESTELLE - star
ESTHER - star
ETTA - controller
EUGENIA - well-born
EUNICE - victorious
EVE - lively
FAITH - trusting
FAY - faithful
FELICITY - happy
FLAVIA - blonde
FLEUR - flower-like
FLORA - flower

# NAME MEANS

FLORENCE - blooming
FRANCES - free
FREDA - peace
GABRIELLE - godly
GAIL - joyful
GAY - merry
GERALDINE - ruler
GERDA - protected
GILDA - servant
GINGER - maidenly
GISELLE - promise
GLADYS - frail

GLORIA - glorious
GREER - watch-woman
HANNAH - full of mercy
HAZEL - commanding
HEATHER - flower
HELEN - light
HELGA - holy
HILDA - warlike
HOLLY - good luck
HOPE - optimistic
IDA - happy
IRENE - peace

LEILA

RACHEL - naive
RITA - pearl
ROSE - rose
RUBY - precious
RUTH - beautiful
SALLY - princess
SHEILA - musical
SHIRLEY - white
SONIA - wise
SUSAN - lily

VIOLET -
VIVIENNE - lively
WANDA - wanderer
WENDY - white
WILLA - desirable
WINNIE - friendly
WYNNE - fair
YVONNE - archer
ZENA - hospitable
ZORA - dawn

IRIS - rainbow
IRMA - strong
IVY - vine
JEAN - God's gift
JEMIMA - dove
JENNIE - fair lady
JERRIE - ruler
JESSIE - rich
LEILA - slave
LILLIAN - lily
LINDA - beautiful
LOLA - strong
LOIS - better
LUCY - light
LYDIA - cultured
MABEL - lovable

MADELINE - strong
MARGARET - pearl
MARTHA - lady
MARY - bitter
MAY - kinswoman
MEGAN - strong
MELODY - song
MERLE - blackbird
MILLIE - strength
MINNA - loving
MONA - alone
MONICA - adviser
MORNA - gentle
MURIEL - bitter
MYRA - wonderful
NORMA - pattern

MARGARET

# THE *Unwanted* FLOWERGIRL

**F**LOSSIE WHITE and Joan Crampton were playing their favourite game of "weddings." With her funny upturned nose, and wearing two old curtains as a wedding dress, Flossie wasn't exactly a beautiful bride, but she was enjoying herself. Joan's mother and elder sister, Pat, were watching the "wedding" when suddenly—

This simple, beautifully illustrated, 'feel good' story was typical of those which found favour with readers in the early sixties.

LOOK OUT, FLOSSIE!

REALLY, FLOSSIE—YOU'RE THE CLUMSIEST GIRL I'VE EVER COME ACROSS! IT'S A GOOD JOB THE VASE DIDN'T BREAK!

I'M SORRY, PAT.

A few days later, Joan came to Flossie with exciting news. Pat was going to be married in three weeks' time—

—AND I'M SURE WE'LL BOTH BE FLOWERGIRLS AT THE WEDDING!

OH, SUPER!

I'LL GET A NICE CARD TO CONGRATULATE PAT, AND I'LL LEAVE IT AT HER HOUSE ON THE WAY HOME—

THE DOOR'S OPEN—I'LL PUT THE CARD ON THE HALLSTAND.

Then Flossie heard voices in the Cramptons' living-room.

FLOSSIE IS A NICE GIRL, BUT NOBODY WOULD SAY SHE'S PRETTY—AND WITH HER BEING SO CLUMSY, SHE'D SPOIL EVERYTHING. I DON'T CARE *WHAT* JOAN HAS TOLD HER—FLOSSIE IS *NOT* GOING TO BE A FLOWERGIRL AT MY WEDDING!

Fighting back the tears, Flossie turned and ran—

PAT WAS RIGHT—I AM *UGLY!*

The Cramptons found Flossie's card where she had let it fall, and they knew that she must have heard them talking. In the days that passed, Flossie and Joan continued to play together, but they never talked about the coming wedding.

Later—

I'LL SEE IF JOAN IS COMING OUT TO PLAY.

JOAN HAS GONE TO THE PAPER SHOP, BUT SHE'LL BE BACK IN A FEW MINUTES. COME IN AND I'LL SHOW YOU PAT'S WEDDING DRESS—IT ARRIVED TODAY.

Being a bridesmaid or flowergirl was something most girls dreamed about.

# GOOD LUCK TO THE BRIDE! WEDDING SUPERSTITIONS

*It wasn't just wedding stories that took a trick with readers. Wedding features were also popular – especially if they combined facts with fun. Here are some typical examples from the sixties.*

The bride's sisters are in danger of suffering trampled tootsies—all because of an old superstition that a bride's elder sisters would never find husbands of their own unless they danced barefoot at the younger girl's wedding.

This bride is getting ready for her wedding, but she won't put on her other glove until she leaves the mirror. She knows that it is considered unlucky for a bride to see a reflection of herself completely dressed for the ceremony.

It is supposed to be unlucky for a bride to walk over the threshold when she goes into her new home for the first time in her married life. The traditional means of entry is for the 'groom to carry his wife in—and that can be hard work!

This girl doesn't care if the people stare. She believes that it is lucky for a bride to wear old shoes at her wedding—and nobody can say THESE shoes are new!

Many years ago, when a Yorkshire bride returned to her father's house after the ceremony, the wedding festivities began with a plate of wedding cake being flung from a window. If the plate didn't break, bad luck would follow the couple in their married life. So everybody here is happy, except the policeman, perhaps!

This young man is being chased away by his future mother-in-law. He is due to be married later on in the day, and Mum knows it is unlucky for a bride to see her husband-to-be on the day of the wedding, before the time of the ceremony.

Why does Miss Perkins refuse to listen to Mr Potts' proposal of marriage? The answer lies in a rhyming superstition dealing with a girl's change of name and initials on marriage:
"Change the name and not the letter,
Change for worse and not for better."

Many early – and later – Bunty stories showed how different girls found individual ways to overcome the obstacles life threw at them. Some used brains or cunning, and others had help from animals or secret benefactors. While travelling through the old 'Wild West', however, young Sadie had her own secret weapon – her sewing machine!

*Josie soon vaulted right to the top of the story polls.*

# '80s

The 1980s brought big changes for Bunty — as these covers illustrate.

Bunty and her dog, Buster, have fun — little knowing that their days are numbered.

No. 1329—July 2, 1983.

## BUNTY

EVERY TUESDAY

16p
IR 23p
(Inc. V.A.T.)

On October 21st, 1989, Bunty changed completely with a new cover design and new size

Every Tuesday

## Bunty
FOR GIRLS

No. 1658
October 21, 1989

30p
(I.R. 46p inc. VAT)

THE FOUR MARYS IN SUPER COLOUR

▼ INSIDE
GIRLS JUST WANNA HAVE FUN!
BROOKIE'S KATIE ROGERS

DESIGN A FASHION
ON THE ROAD STREET INTERVIEW
COLOUR PHOTO STORY

KYLIE MINOG PIN-UF

Every Tuesday

No. 1661
November 11, 1989

## Bunty
FOR GIRLS

30p
(I.R. 46p inc. VAT)

BAD NEWS FOR THE TWINS!
read THE COMP

▼ INSIDE ▼
FUZZBOX P•I•N•U•P
KYLIE— SHE'S SO LUCKY, LUCKY, LUCKY!

The revamped style gave space to publicise the contents.

# COSY CORNER

Hi, girls!

January sales are not much fun when you don't have any money to spend, are they? Here's an easy way to earn some extra cash —write to me! If your letter gets printed, I'll send you £2

But remember—your entry MUST be original

Send your entry, naming your three favourite stories, to, "Cosy Corner," "Bunty," 20 Cathcart Street, Kentish Town, London, NW5 3BN.

Your chum,

*Bunty*

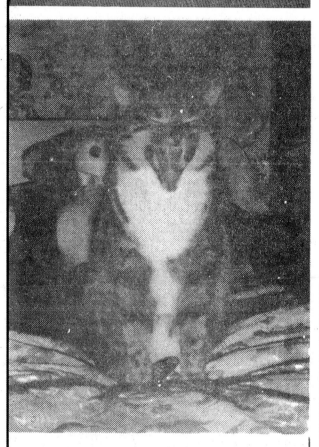

## ZUKI

*My cat, Zuki, was sound asleep on my bed when I woke her up to take this photograph.*
**—Alexandra Chambers, Belfast.**

BTY 29.1.83

## TREND SETTER

I was reading a book which described the heroine's shoes which were in the latest fashion. My mum came in shortly afterwards and showed me the shoes which she had just bought. They were exactly the same as the ones described in my book. Nothing unusual in that, you might think, but the book I was reading was a historical novel and the heroine lived in the time of King Charles—over three hundred years ago!
**—Leslie T. Morris, Brimfield.**

## MEMORIES

Last summer, my family and I went on holiday to France. We had a lovely time visiting many interesting places. One of the places we found most interesting was Mont St. Michel, a tiny island which we crossed to by a causeway. On Mont St. Michel, we went to the monastery and saw the monks who live there.

On our way home, we stopped off in London for a week and while there, we saw the hit show "Annie", Buckingham Palace, Downing Street and Clarence House, the Queen Mother's residence.
**—Mary Wild, Keighley.**

## DECKED OUT!

This is my dog Lindy who is a wire-haired fox terrier. She's eight years old. Doesn't she look cute sitting in the deck chair?
**—Nicola Godfrey, Wakefield.**

## LUCKY?

I was walking with my mum and she said, "Touch wood, it's lucky!" After saying that she touched a nearby fence and got a splinter in her finger!
**—Susan Tailby, Leicester**

## SILLY GRAN

One night when I was staying with my gran, we settled down to watch a spaghetti western on TV. My gran came through with some tea, looked at the TV and said, "Oh, good! It's one of those macaroni movies!"
**—Joanne McLean, Inverness.**

## THE LAWNMOWER

*Our pet goat, June, seen with me in this photograph, is known as "The Lawnmower" by our family because she keeps the grass cut by eating it. We have to watch her carefully, though, because if we don't, she would eat the flower beds too!*

**—Fiona Lyall, Stowmarket.**

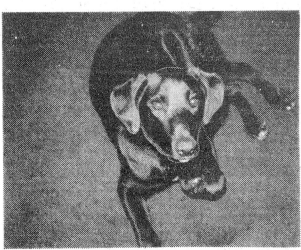

## FRED

My dog is called Fred, and I took this photograph of him especially for "Cosy Corner!"

**—Fiona Newman, London.**

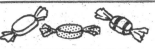

## SWEET TALK

When I was younger, my mum had a friend in for coffee one day and I kept interrupting them. I interrupted for about the sixth time shouting, "Mummy!" My mum was really annoyed with me and said, "Stop calling out 'Mummy'! I'm fed-up!" A little later I turned round and said, "Fed-up, can I have some sweets, please?

**—Melanie Smith, Wisbech.**

## WELL FILLED!

A friend of my brother's invited him to spend the day at his home. Later that evening, when my brother came home, Mum asked him what he had been given for dinner. "Cushions with meat in them!" he replied. He meant ravioli!

**—Zana, London.**
*(Please send me your full name, Zana.)*

**Please tell your parents before replying to stamp advertisements.**

*Cosy Corner was still an important part of the magazine in the eighties — but by then the style had changed enormously. The layout was now much looser with readers' photographs playing an ever increasing part — and prizes had changed, with no mention of the Bunty scarf anywhere. Jenny Wren had also disappeared, leaving it to Bunty herself to communicate with the readers.*

*Some final fun with The Four Marys. This story comes from 1989 and is in full, vibrant colour.*

Later—

PHEW — THEY'RE ALL IN BED NOW! WONDER WHERE COTTY AND MISS CREEF ARE?

Just then —

HA! HA! IT'S COTTY AND MISS CREEF — DRESSED AS SANTAS! AND THEY'VE GOT A NEW BIKE FOR SALLY — LOOK!

IT'S FANTASTIC! SALLY WILL LOVE IT.

AND LOOK WHAT ELSE WE'VE GOT.

SANTA OUTFITS FOR YOU ALL!

WELL, THANK GOODNESS THAT'S OVER! IT'S HARD WORK WRAPPING PRESENTS!

HEY — IT'S CHRISTMAS DAY. WE CAN OPEN OUR OWN PRESENTS NOW.

MY MUM SENT ME THIS SUPER RADIO CASSETTE. WHAT DID YOU GET, COTTY?

YES, YOU'VE BEEN VERY SECRETIVE, COTTY.

MY GRAN SENT ME MONEY TO TREAT MYSELF TO A NEW HAIRSTYLE, SO I DID. I WAS GETTING FED UP OF THOSE PIGTAILS ANYWAY.

30.12.89 BTY

Later —

MERRY CHRISTMAS, EVERYONE!

★ ★ ★ A happy ending for all. ★ ★ ★

With the rising popularity of television 'soap operas', it was only natural that story magazines would follow suit. The two stories shown here were hugely popular with readers during the later years of Bunty.

The COMP

THE twins' mother had been involved in a serious road accident. Looking after the family had put so much pressure on their step-sister, Angie, that her engagement to Mark Davis had broken off—

IT'S ONLY MY SHOES . . .

FOR GOODNESS' SAKE, CAN'T YOU PICK UP AFTER YOURSELF, BECKY? YOU'RE WORSE THAN THE KIDS FOR LEAVING STUFF UNDERFOOT!

This story revolved round the daily life and family problems of a group of girls attending Redvale Comp. It had been a popular story in Nikki, a sister magazine, and moved to Bunty in 1989.

PHONE FOR YOU,

FOR MISS ANGE

Later, the

LOO
FLOWE
ISN'T TH
KI

Luv, Lisa

I COULDN'T WAIT TO TELL DEBBIE ALL ABOUT MARK GOING OUT WITH LUCY WALKER — BOO, HOO!

Late '89 also saw the start of a radical new photo story soap based round the stories from a young girl's diary.

OH, I KNOW LUCY WALKER, LISA. HER SISTER'S IN CLASS 9 AT OUR SCHOOL.

REALLY?

OH, NO! NATALIE WALKER! SHE'S IN THE CHOIR WITH ME! HOPE SHE DOESN'T KNOW I FANCIED MARK!

*The final weekly issue of Bunty appeared on February 17th, 2001. The appearance of the magazine had changed dramatically over the 2249 issues, and some stories had given way to features, puzzles and quizzes. One thing remained constant, however, and The Four Marys, Bunty's favourite schoolgirls from issue No1, were still around to say goodbye.*